NATIONAL GEOGRAP

Reac[h]™ for Reading

COMMON CORE PROGRAM

NATIONAL GEOGRAPHIC LEARNING | CENGAGE Learning

NATIONAL GEOGRAPHIC LEARNING | CENGAGE Learning

Acknowledgments
Grateful acknowledgment is given to the authors, artists, photographers, museums, publishers, and agents for permission to reprint copyrighted material. Every effort has been made to secure the appropriate permission. If any omissions have been made or if corrections are required, please contact the Publisher.

Cover Design and Art Direction: Visual Asylum

Cover illustration: Joel Sotelo

Illustration Credits: All illustrations by National Geographic Learning

Photographic Credits: PM2.2 (all) John Paul Endress; **PM2.6** (all) Clem Spalding; **PM2.22** (all) Clem Spalding; **PM4.2a–PM4.2b** Clem Spalding; **PM5.13** (tl, cl, cr, bl) Photodisc/Getty Images, (tc) Peter Sherrard/Getty Images, (tr) Clem Spalding,; **PM5.13a** (tl) Clem Spalding, (tr, cr, bl, bg,) Photodisc/Getty Images, (br) Marian Bacon/Animals Animals; **PM5.23** (tl) Chase Swift/Corbis, (tr) Jeff Rotman/ Getty Images, (cl, c) Photodisc/Getty Images, (bl) Stuart Westmoreland/Getty Images; **PM5.23b** (tl) Pat Hermansen/ Getty Images, (tr) Photodisc/Getty Images, (cr, bl, br) Getty Images; **PM6.2a** (tl) Peter Johnson/Corbis, (tr) Clem Spalding, (bl) James L. Amos/Corbis; **PM6.2b** (tl) Darrel Gulin/Corbis, (tl) Erick Hosking/Corbis, (cr, bl) David Spears/ Corbis; **PM 6.12** (all) Clem Spalding; **PM6.31a** (tl) Jim Cumins/Getty Images, (tr) Elyse Lewin/Getty Images, (bl, br) Photodisc/Getty Images; **PM6.31b** (tl, tr, cl) Stockbyte, (cr, bl) Clem Spalding, (br) Author Tilley/Getty Images; **PM 7.2a** (tl, tr, cl) Clem Spalding, (bg) Emily Wamsteker/AP Photo, (bl, bc) Getty Images; **PM7.2b** (tl, tr, bl, br) Clem Spalding, (bg) Emily Wamsteker/AP Photo, (cr) Getty Images; **PM7.12a–PM7.12b** Clem Spalding; PM9.3 (tl) Getty Images, (tr) Clem Spalding.

For product information and technology assistance, contact us at **Customer & Sales Support, 888-915-3276**

For permission to use material from this text or product, submit all requests online at **www.cengage.com/permissions**
Further permissions questions can be emailed to **permissionrequest@cengage.com**

National Geographic Learning | Cengage Learning
1 Lower Ragsdale Drive
Building 1, Suite 200
Monterey, CA 93940

Cengage Learning is a leading provider of customized learning solutions with office locations around the globe, including Singapore, the United Kingdom, Australia, Mexico, Brazil, and Japan. Locate your local office at **www.cengage.com/global**.

Cengage Learning products are represented in Canada by Nelson Education, Ltd.

Visit National Geographic Learning online at **NGL.Cengage.com**
Visit our corporate website a **www.cengage.com**

Printed in the USA.
Sheridan, KY, A CJK Group Company

ISBN: 978-1-305-49895-2 (Practice Book)

ISBN: 978-1-305-65867-7 (Practice Masters)

Printed in the United States of America

21 22 23 24 25

18 17 16 15

ontents

nit 1: Step Into School

eek 1

eek 2

Unit 2: My Family and Me

ːit 3: Visit the Farm!

Unit 4: All Kinds of Plants

Name ______________________________

Alphabet Knowledge

Learn the Alphabet

Aa Bb Cc Dd

Ee Ff Gg

Hh Ii Jj Kk

Ll Mm Nn Oo Pp

Qq Rr Ss

Tt Uu Vv

Ww Xx Yy Zz

Directions: Have children cut out each strip and mix up the strips. Then sing the alphabet song and have children put the strips in the correct order.

Name ______________________________

Concepts of Print

Letter Cards

E	J	O	T	Y	
D	I	N	S	X	
C	H	M	R	W	
B	G	L	Q	V	
A	F	K	P	U	Z

Directions: Have children cut out the letters for use in letter recognition and matching activities. Children can store their letters in resealable plastic bags.

Name ____________________

Concepts of Print

Letter Cards

e	j	o	t	y	
d	i	n	s	x	
c	h	m	r	w	
b	g	l	q	v	
a	f	k	p	u	z

Directions: Have children cut out the letters for use in letter recognition and matching activities. Children can store their letters in resealable plastic bags.

Name ______________________________

Comprehension

Compare Details

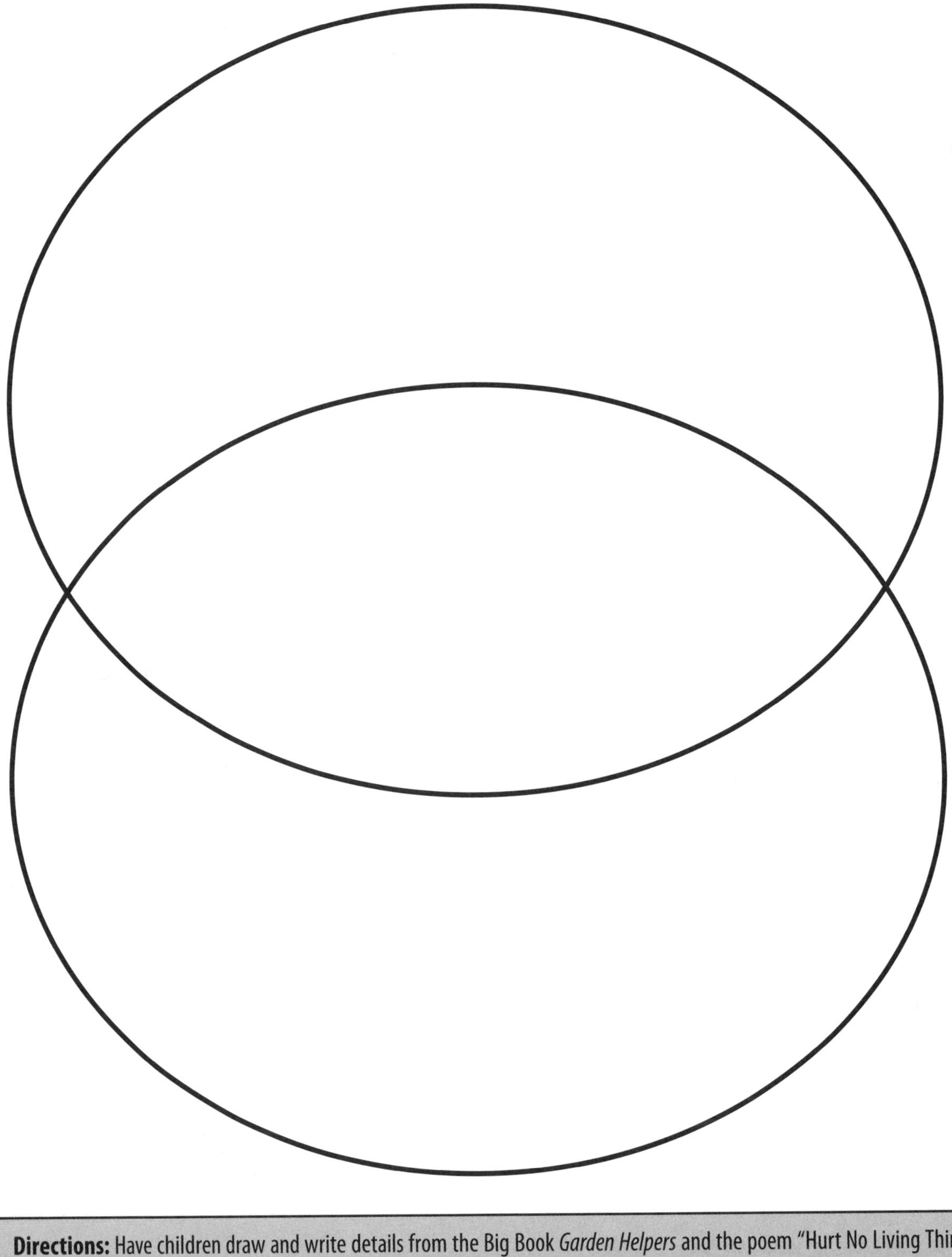

Directions: Have children draw and write details from the Big Book *Garden Helpers* and the poem "Hurt No Living Thing" to show how the two selections are the same and different.

Name ______________________________

Phonics and High Frequency Words

Read Sentences

1. I am big.
   I can go in here.

2. I go here.
   I bit this.

3. See Kim.
   Kim bit it.

4. Mom and I can
   go here.

Directions: Discuss the pictures. Have partners read the sentences.

Name ______________________

Grammar

Verbs

boy read

brush teeth

sing dad

ducks swim

fly high

fun dance

Directions: Discuss each picture with children. Read aloud the two words below each picture. Have children circle the word that tells about the action in the picture.

Name ______________________________

Phonics

Blend Words with b

1. It is big.

2. This is a bat.

3. I see a bib.

4. I see a bag.

Directions: Have children read each sentence and draw a line to the picture it matches.

Name ____________________

Comprehension

Main Idea and Details

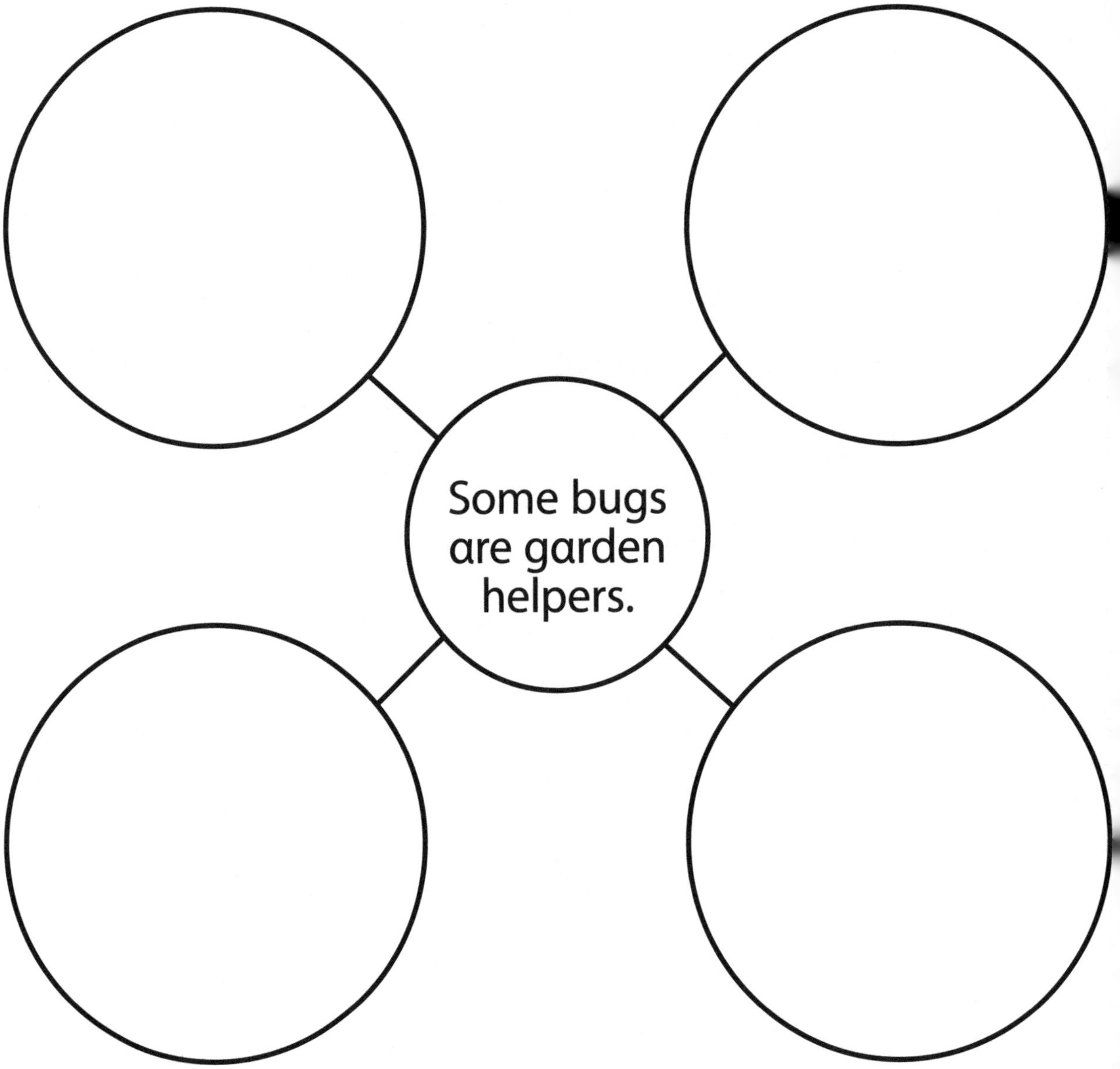

Directions: Discuss the main idea of *Garden Helpers* with children. Read aloud the text in the center circle of the graphic organizer. Then have children draw or write four supporting details from the essay in the outer circles.

Name ______________________________

High Frequency Words

Read Sentences

High Frequency **Word**
go

1. I go in here.

2. Can I go in here?

3. See him go!

4. Can I go in here?

5. I go and go!

Directions: Discuss the pictures. Have partners read the sentences together.

My Book of B b

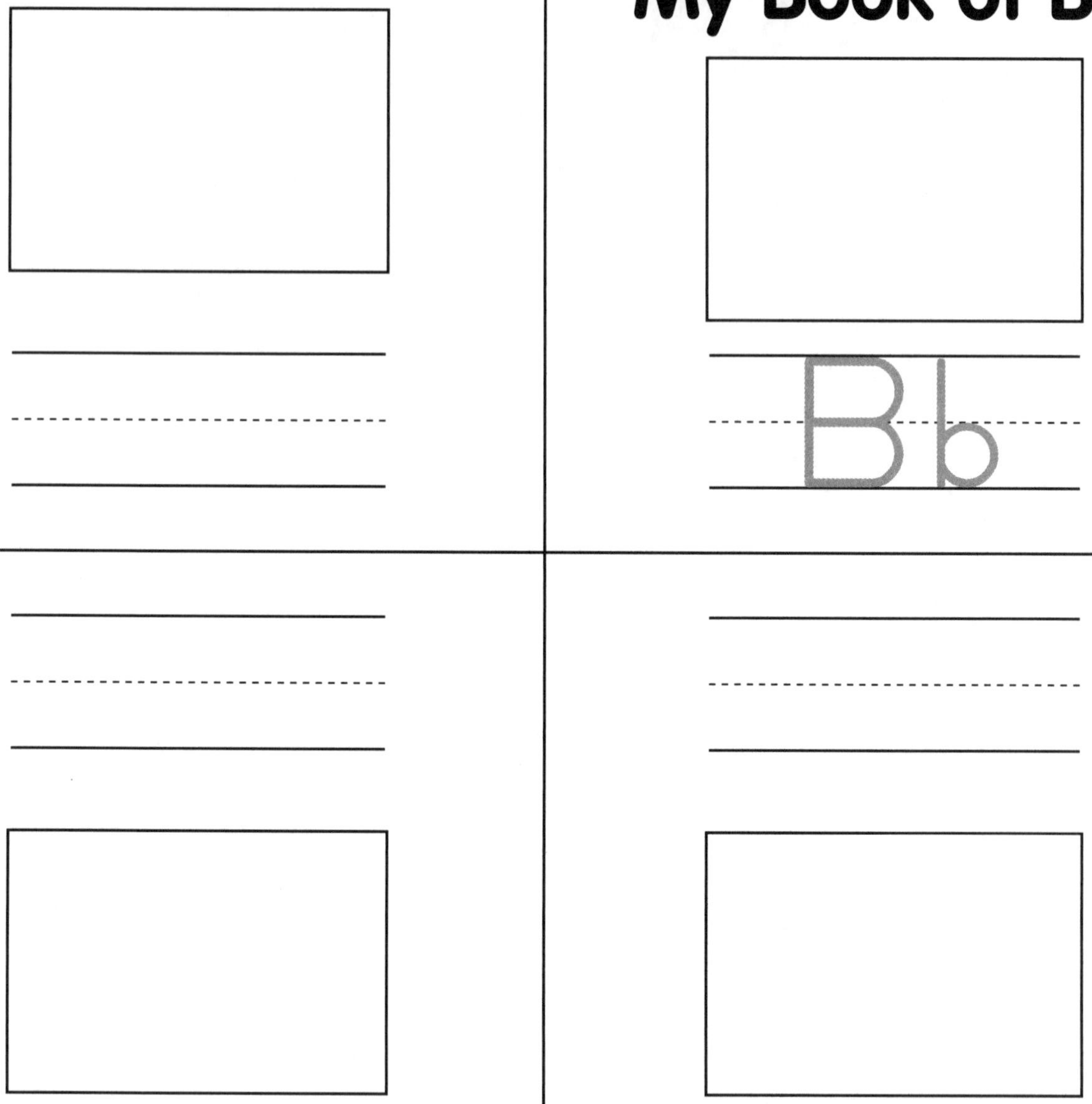

tions: Have children trace the letter forms with a finger as you model letter formation. Then have children name and cut out the cards. hem group the cards that start with the sound for *b* and paste one card on each page. Children can write *Bb* to label their pictures.

Name ______________________

High Frequency Words

Word Cards

High Frequency Word
go

his	a	and	go
ee	I	for	go
.	Is	here	go
?	see	a	go

Directions: Duplicate and cut out the word cards for use during practice activities.

Bb

bee

bow

and a bear on a bus.

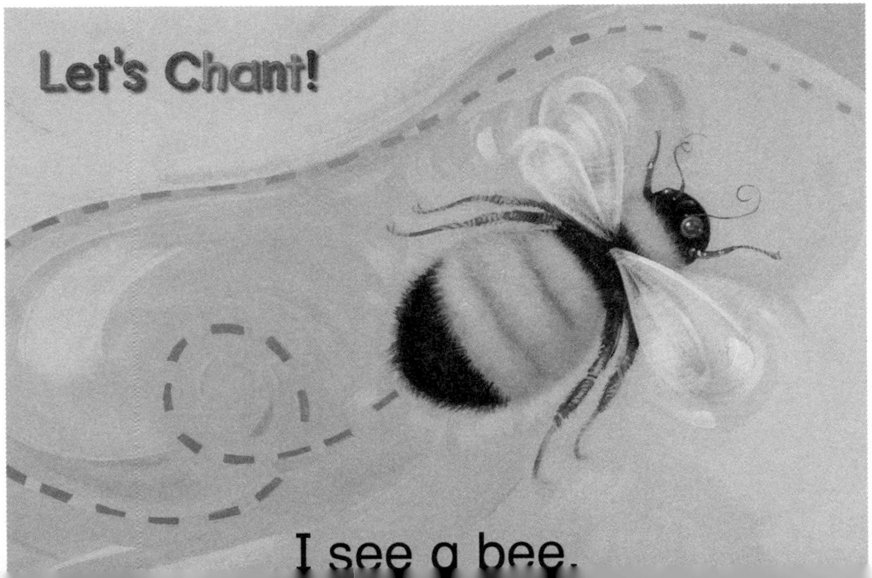

I see a bee.

a bee on a bow

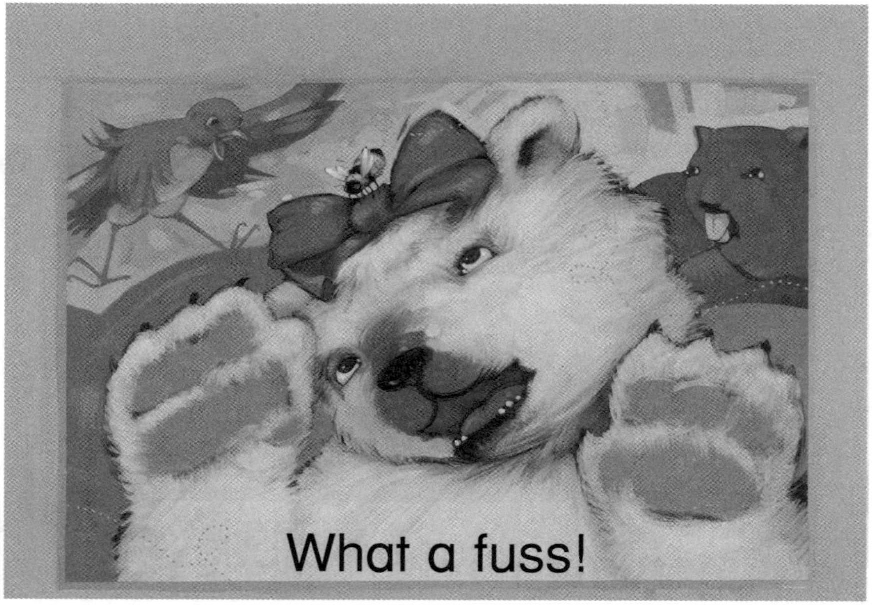

What a fuss!

Alphachant™

Bb

by Lada Kratky
illustrated by Lori Lohstoeter

HAMPTON-BROWN

a bow on a bear.

Bb

bear

bus

Name ____________________

Phonics

Sound for b

1. 	**2.** 	**3.** 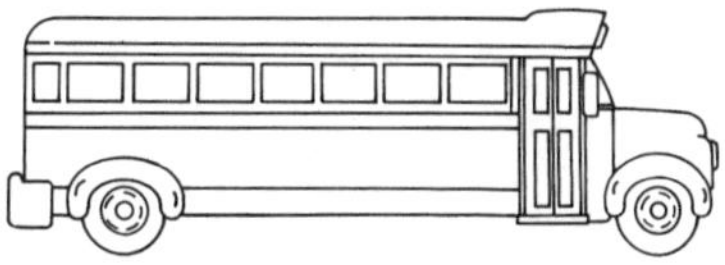
4. 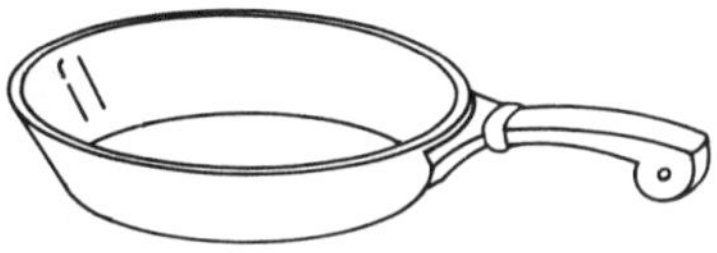	**5.** 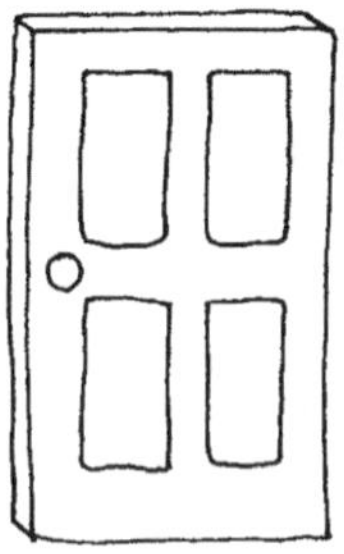	**6.** 
7. 	**8.** 	**9.** 

ions: Name each picture with children. Have children color the pictures whose names begin with *b*.

Name ________________________________

Comprehension

Sequence

First:

Next:

Last:

Directions: Have children draw three steps to make something of their choice, as in the selections *How to Grow a Garden* and *Apples*.

Name ______________________________

Phonics and High Frequency Words

Read Sentences

High Frequency Word
here

1. Is it in here?

2. Fit this in the gap.

3. Is gas in this?

4. I like it here!

Directions: Have partners read the sentences. Discuss the pictures.

Name ______________________________

Grammar

Verbs

Directions: Have children draw a picture of themselves doing an action. Then have them write an action word (verb) to tell about what they are doing.

Name ______________________________

Phonics

Blend Words with g

1. Gas is in this.

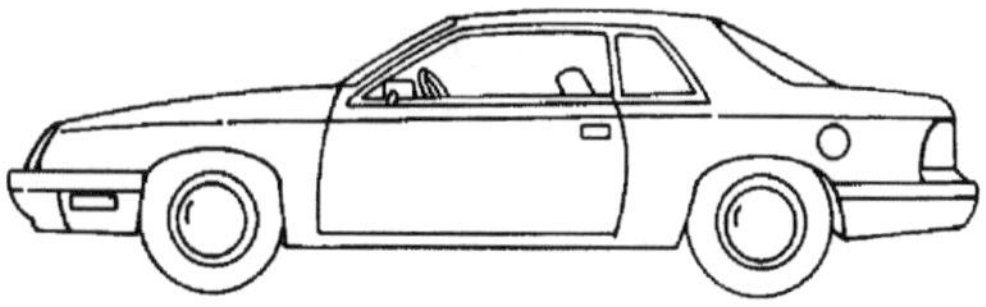

2. It can fit in the gap.

3. Gas is in here.

4. Can this fit in the gap?

Directions: Review the meaning of *gap:* "a hole in something." Have children read each sentence. Discuss the pictures.

Name ______________________________

Comprehension

Sequence

First:

Next:

Last:

Directions: Have children draw steps to tell what to do *first, next,* and *last* to make an apple pie. Then have them discuss the steps. Children's sequences will vary.

Name ____________________

High Frequency Words

Read Sentences

High Frequency Word
here

1. I look in here for him.

2. I can fit this in here.

3. I sit here.

4. I nap here. I like it!

Directions: Discuss the pictures. Have partners read the sentences together.

My Book of Gg

Gg

ons: Have children trace the letter forms with a finger as you model letter formation. Then have children name and cut out the cards. em group the cards that start with the sound for *g* and paste one card on each page. Children can write *Gg* to label their pictures.

Name ____________________

High Frequency Words

Word Cards

High Frequency Word
here

I	for	here	here
!	Here	a	here
,	is	like	here
.	a	and	here

Directions: Duplicate and cut out the word cards for use during practice activities.

Gg

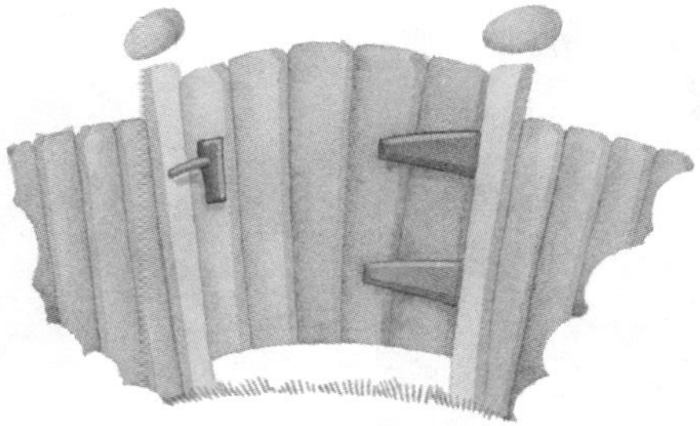

gate

goat

The gorilla goes in the gate,

Let's Chant!

The garden gate is open

The goat goes in the gate

but he's too late!

8

Alphachant™

Gg

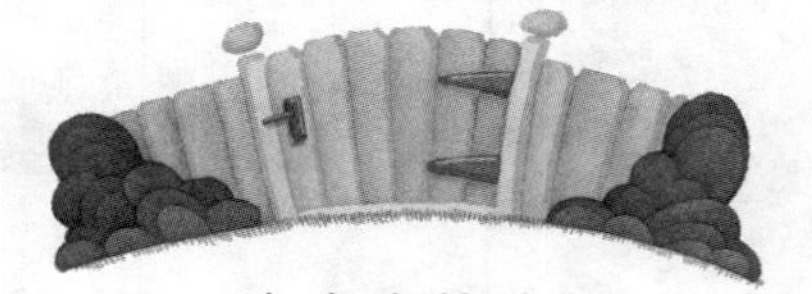

by Lada Kratky
illustrated by Peter Grosshauser

HAMPTON-BROWN

1

The goose goes in the gate

Gg

goose

gorilla

Name ______________________

Phonics

Sound for g

Gg

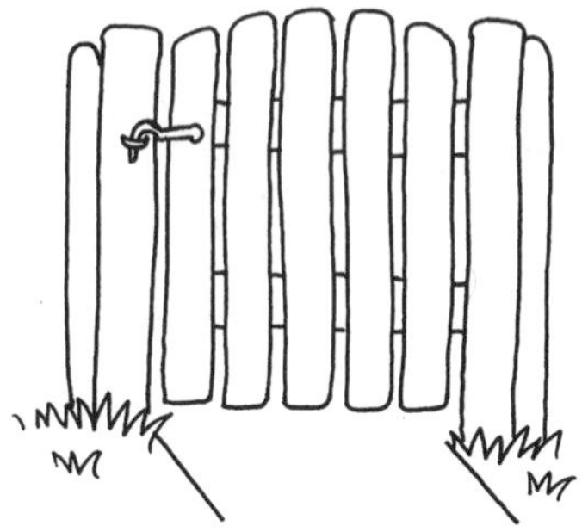

ctions: Name the letter and each picture with children. Have children cut out the cards. Ask partners to sort by beginning sound, ping the pictures with the beginning sound for *g* with the *Gg* card. Then, have partners name all of the pictures in the *Gg* group.

Name ______________________________

Comprehension

Compare Sequences

Directions: After discussing what happened in *The Little Red Hen* and *Just One Seed,* have children draw and write about what happened first, next, and last in one of the stories.

Name ______________________

Phonics and High Frequency Words

Read Sentences

1. This is Sam and Fan.

2. This is for Fan!

3. Fan can fit this in.

4. Sam and I fit this in.

Directions: Discuss the pictures. Have partners read the sentences.

Name ______________________________

Grammar

Verbs

Directions: Have children color the page. Then have a partner act out an action they see or other actions that might happen in the ga
The other partner should then guess the action. Have partners add a new character to the picture for each new action they name.

Name ______________________________

Phonics

Blend Words with f

1. This is a fan.

2. Is this cat fat?

3. This can fit a man.

4. This has a fin.

Directions: Have children read each sentence and draw a line to the picture it matches.

Name ______________________

Comprehension

Sequence

Directions: Have children draw a picture of what happens last in *Just One Seed*. Then help them write a sentence to tell about the event.

Name ______________________

High Frequency Words

Read Sentences

High Frequency Word
for

1. This is for a rat.	**2.** This hat is for a man.
3. This mat is for a cat.	**4.** This pin is for a rip.

Directions: Have children read each sentence and draw a picture to match. Have partners read the sentences and share their pictures.

My Book of Ff

Ff

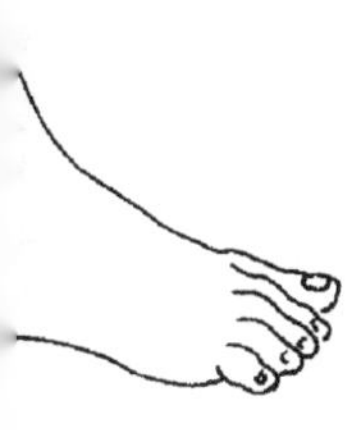

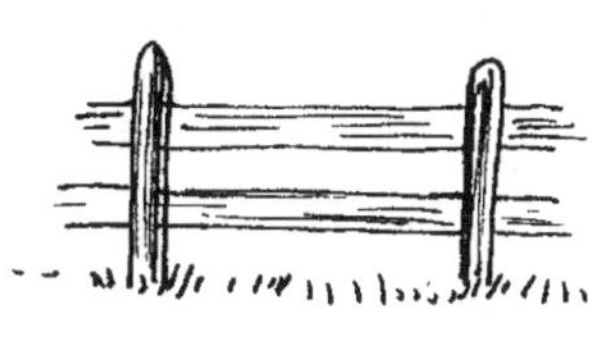

ions: Have children trace the letter forms with a finger as you model letter formation. Then have children name and cut out the cards. em group the cards that start with the sound for *f* and paste one card on each page. Children can write *Ff* to label their pictures.

Name ____________________

High Frequency Words

Word Cards

High Frequency Word
for

ok	is	for	for
ny	like	This	for
ok	and	a	for
.	I	for	for

Directions: Duplicate and cut out the word cards for use during practice activities.

Ff

fox forest

past the farm,

Let's Chant!

Run fast, mama fox,

through the forest.

into your den. Home again.

Alphachant™

Ff

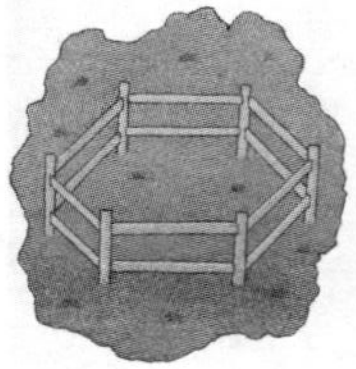

by Lada Kratky
illustrated by Stefano Vitale

HAMPTON-BROWN

under the fence.

Ff

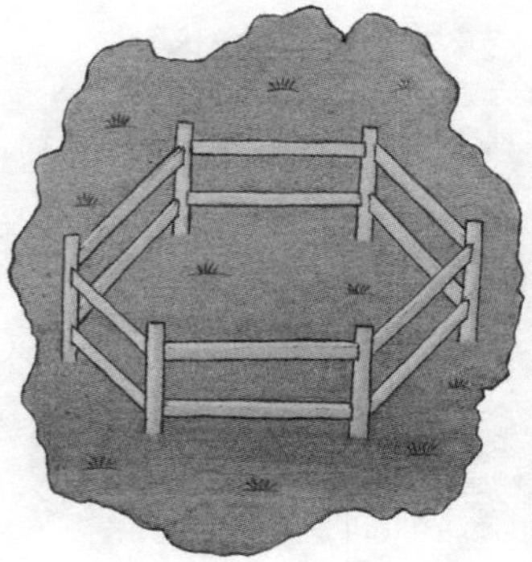

fence

farm

Name ______________________________

Phonics

Sound for f

1. 	**2.** 	**3.** 
4. 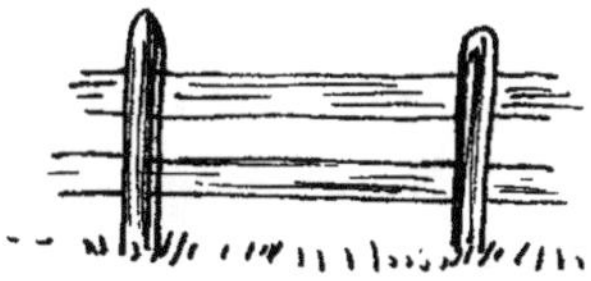	**5.** 	**6.** 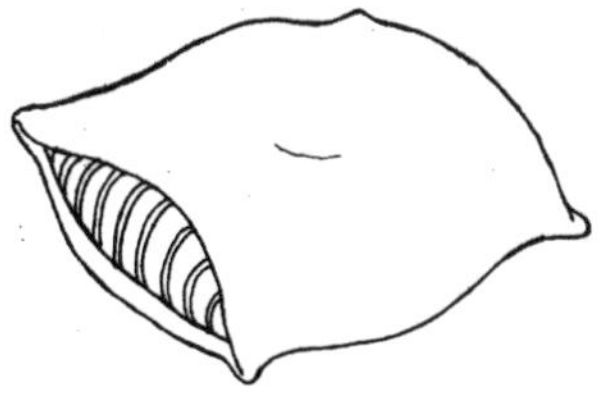
7. 	**8.** 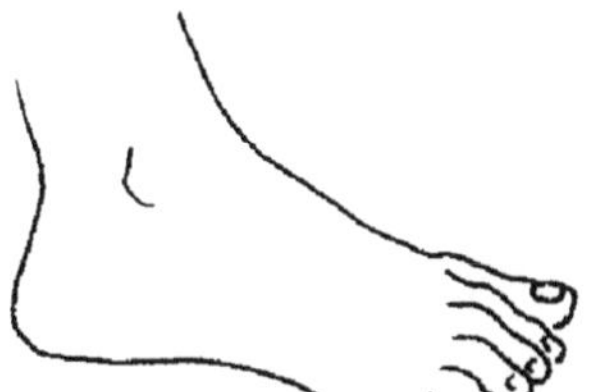	**9.** 

Directions: Name each picture with children. Have children color the pictures whose names begin with *f*.

Name ______________________

Comprehension

Compare Fairy Tales

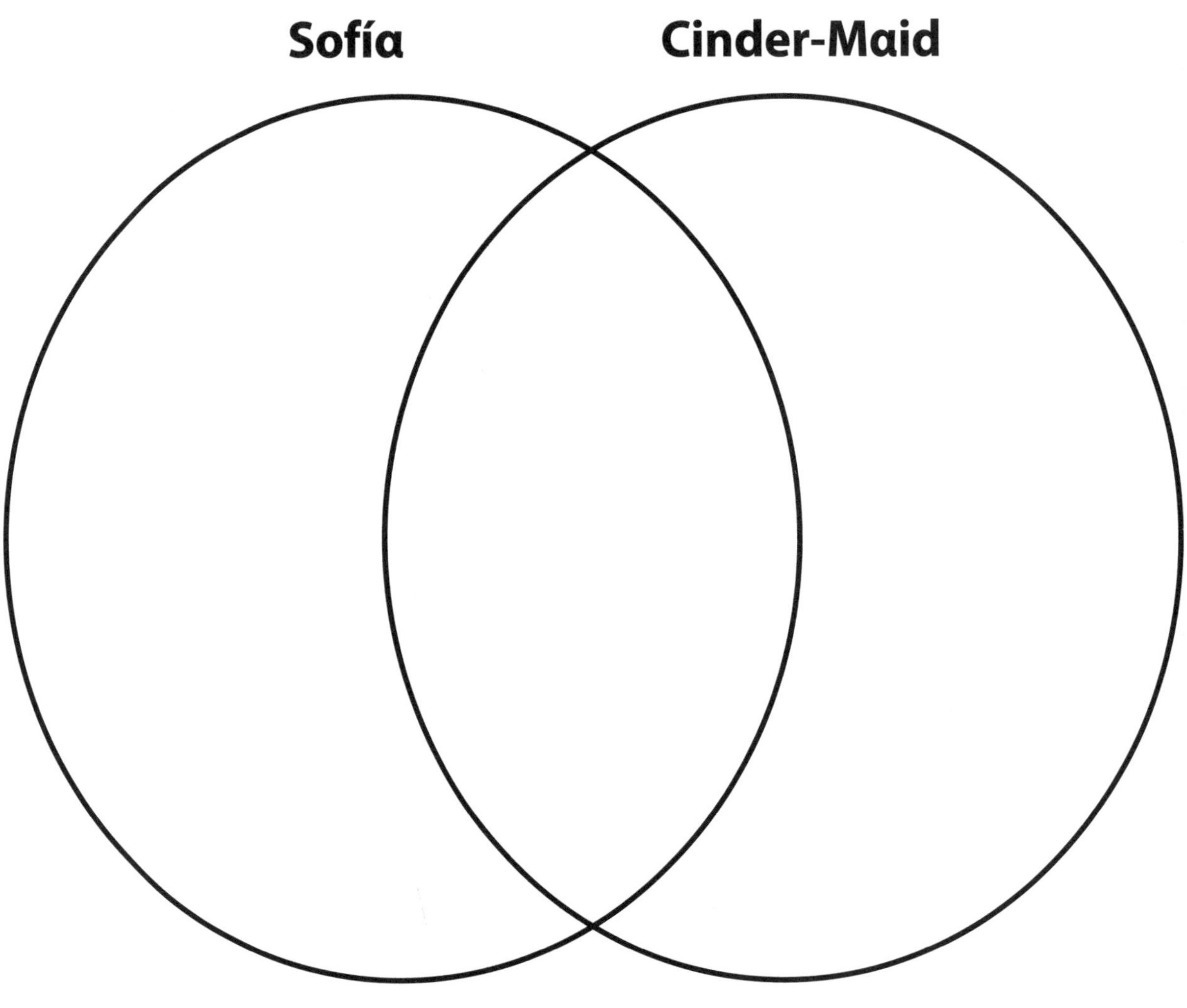

Directions: Have children use pictures and words to tell how the fairy tales *Sofía and the Sunflower* and *Cinder-Maid and the Oak Tree* are alike and different. Children can draw on a separate piece of paper as needed.

Name ______________________

Phonics and High Frequency Words

Read Sentences

1. See Min sit and look.

2. Min can see this.

3. Min can see this and this.

4. Hap and Pam and Tim see Min.

Directions: Discuss the pictures. Have partners read the sentences together.

Name ______________________________

Grammar

Verbs

Directions: Have children use action words (verbs) in sentences to tell a partner what each person in the illustration is doing. Then have them add the labels *water, pick, put, dig,* and *plant* to the picture as they are able.

Name ______________________________

Phonics

Blend Words with i

1. This is Tim.	
2. Tim can sit.	
3. This is Sam.	
4. Can Sam sit in it?	

Directions: Have children read the sentences. Then have them label the characters Tim and Sam.

Name ____________________

Comprehension

Cause and Effect

Cause	Effect

Directions: Have children think of something that happens in the story *Sofía and the Sunflower.* Ask them to draw what happens (the e
in the right-hand box and why it happens (the cause) in the left-hand box. Encourage children to label their drawings.

Name ______________________________

High Frequency Words

Read Sentences

High Frequency **Word**
and

1. Look at this.

2. I see this and this.

3. Look at this and this.

4. I like this. Mmm!

Directions: Discuss the pictures. Have partners read the sentences together.

My Book of Ii

Ii

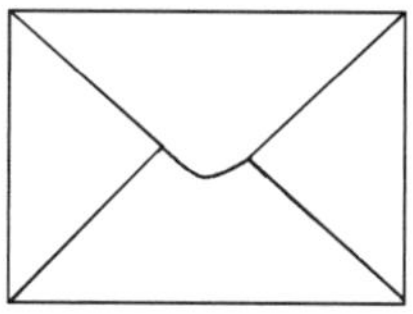

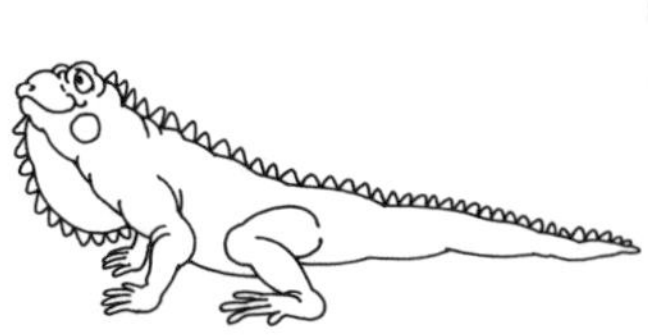

ons: Have children trace the letter forms with a finger as you model letter formation. Then have children name and cut out the cards. em group the cards that start with the sound for *i* and paste one card on each page. Children can write *Ii* to label their pictures.

Name ____________________

High-Frequency Words

Word Cards

High Frequency **Word**
and

ne	This	this	and
ap	I	is	and
.	look	like	and
?	see	a	and

Directions: Duplicate and cut out the word cards and punctuation cards for use during practice activities.

Ii

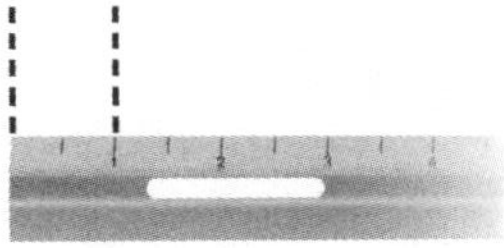

inch   inchworm

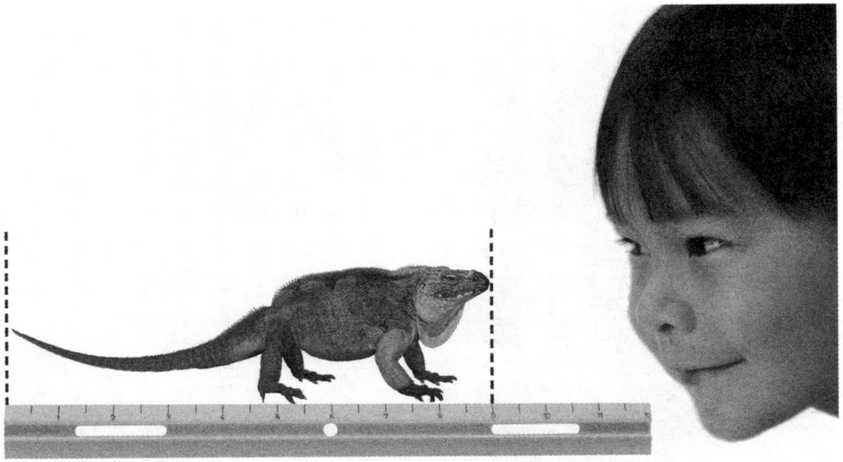

Is an iguana an inch?

Let's Chant!

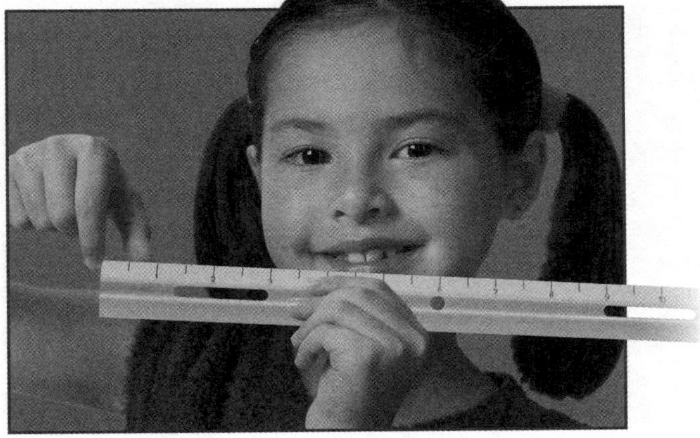

An inch is an inch.

Is an inchworm an inch?

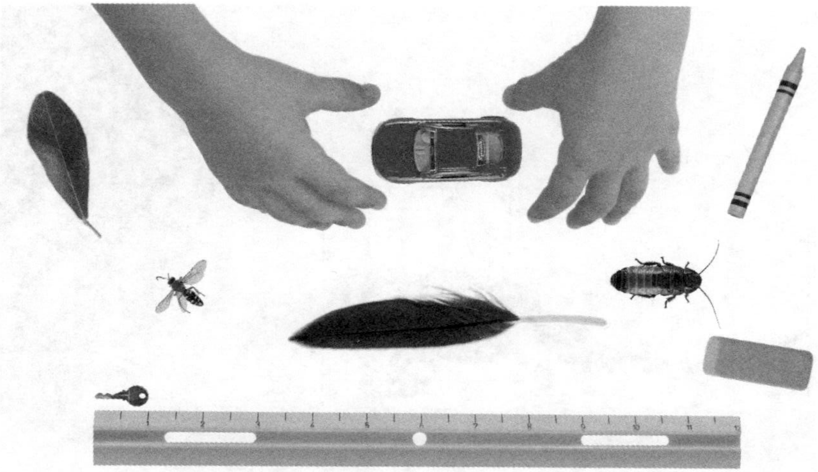

An inch is an inch!

Alphachant™

Ii

by Lada Kratky
photographed by Clem Spalding

HAMPTON-BROWN

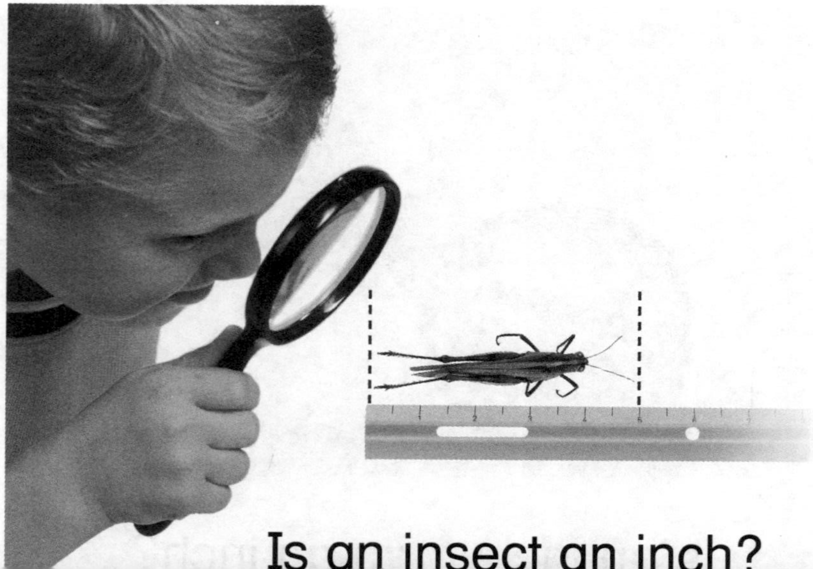

Is an insect an inch?

Ii

insect iguana

Name ______________________________

Phonics

Sound for Ii

I i

ns: Name the letter and each picture with children. Have children cut out the cards. Ask partners to sort by middle sound, grouping es with the middle sound for *i* with the *Ii* card. Have partners name all of the pictures in the *Ii* group.

Name ______________________________

Comprehension

Compare Texts

Directions: After comparing *A World of Animals* and "A House for Me," have children draw and write about one way the selections are alike.

Name ______________________

Phonics and High Frequency Words

Read Sentences

1. A ram can look like this.	**2.** A rat can look like this.
3. The ram ran like this.	**4.** The rat ran like this.

Directions: Have children read each sentence and draw a picture to match. Have partners take turns reading the sentences and showing their pictures.

Name ______________________

Grammar

Antonyms

Directions: Help children contrast two animals using antonyms. Then have children draw pictures of the animals to show their opposite meanings. Children can label their pictures with the antonyms.

Name ______________________________

Phonics

Blend Words with r

1. ram

2. pan

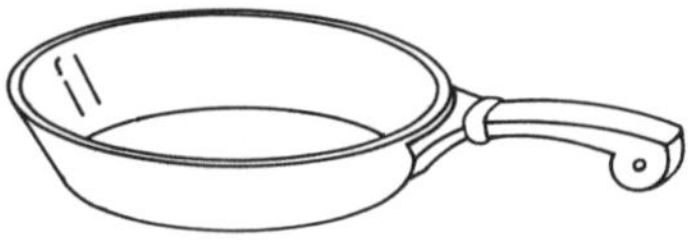

3. rat

4. man

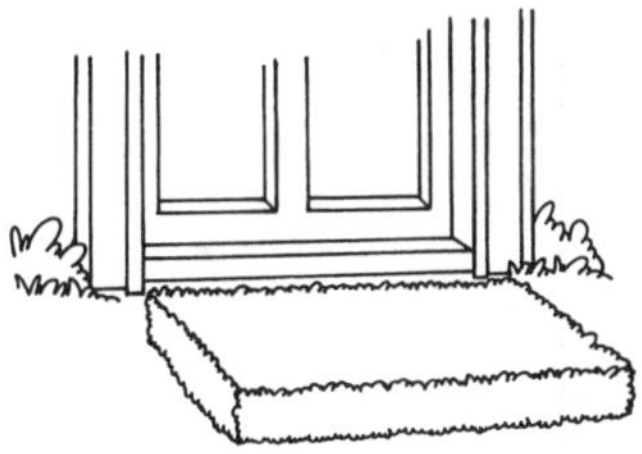

5. ran

Directions: Have children read each word and circle the picture that matches the word.

Name ______________________________

Comprehension

Compare Animals

______________________ ______________________

Directions: Have children write the names of two animals they read about. Talk with them about ways in which the two animals are alike. Then have them draw one idea in the box.

Name ______________________

High Frequency Words

Complete Sentences

High Frequency Word
like

1. Look at this ______.

2. This ______ is like this ______.

3. Look at this ______.

4. Is this ______ like this ______?

Directions: Discuss the pictures and name each item. Have partners take turns completing each pair of sentences orally.

My Book of R r

Rr

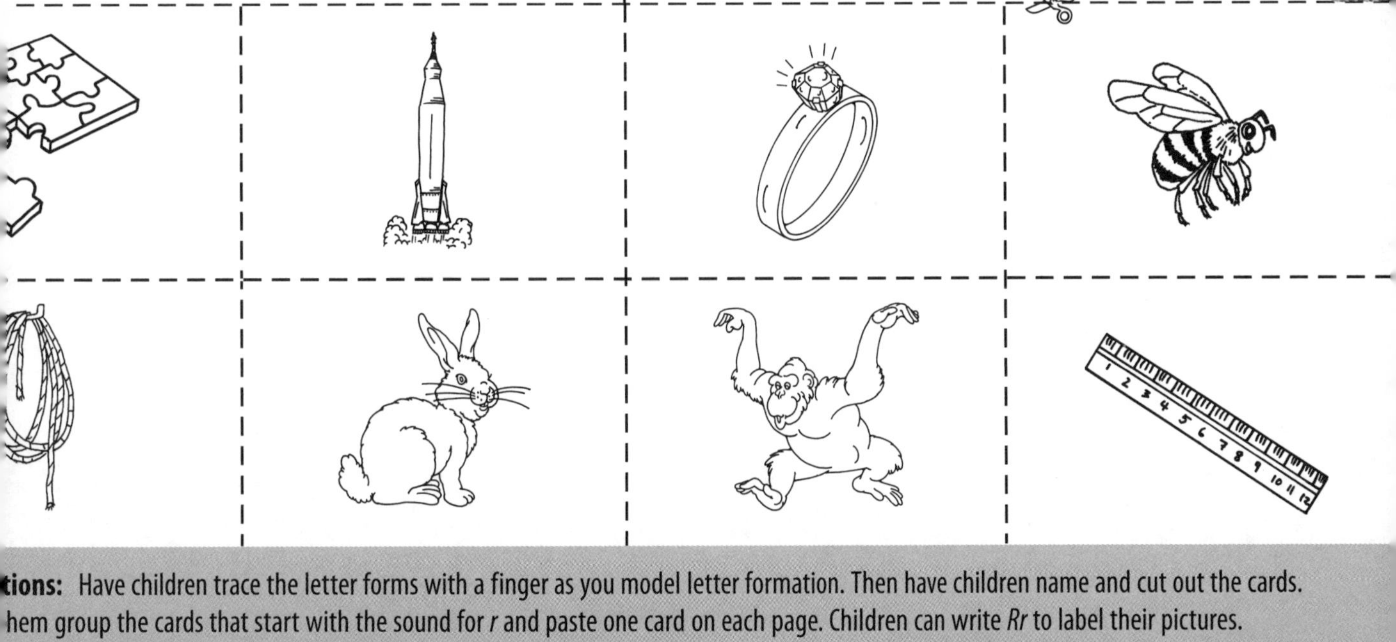

tions: Have children trace the letter forms with a finger as you model letter formation. Then have children name and cut out the cards. hem group the cards that start with the sound for *r* and paste one card on each page. Children can write *Rr* to label their pictures.

Name ______________________________

Phonics and High-Frequency Words

Letter and Word Cards

High Frequency **Word**
like

.	.	like	like
ke	this	like	like
a	is	like	like
ook	This	like	like

Directions: Duplicate and cut out the word and period cards. Each child will need one of each card for use during practice activities.

Rr

rain

roof

2

rain on the rose,

7

I like rain

Rain on the roof

rain on my nose!

8

Alphachant™

Rr

by Lada Kratky
illustrated by Gerardo Suzán

HAMPTON-BROWN

rain on the rabbit

Rr

rabbit

rose

Name ______________________________

Phonics

Sound for r

1. 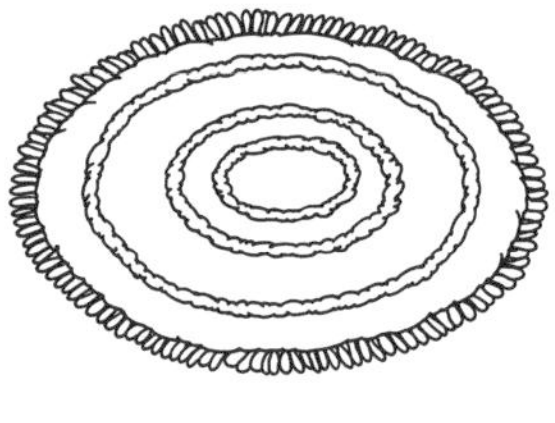	2. 	3. 
4. 	5. 	6. 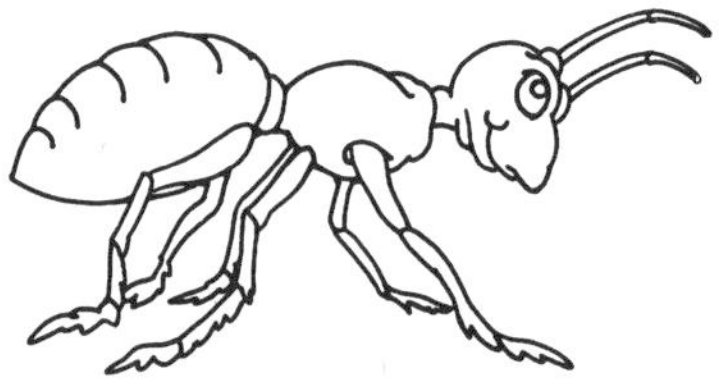
7. 	8. 	9. 

Directions: Name each picture with children. Have children color the pictures whose names begin with the sound for the letter *r*.

Name ____________________

Comprehension

Compare Texts

Directions: After comparing *Baby Names* and "Baby Animals," have children draw and write about one way the selections are alike.

Name ______________________

Phonics and High Frequency Words

Read Sentences

1. I see this hat.

2. This hat is for me!

3. Look at this hat.

4. This hat is for Nan!

Directions: Discuss the pictures. Have partners read the sentences together.

Name ______________________________

Grammar

Antonyms

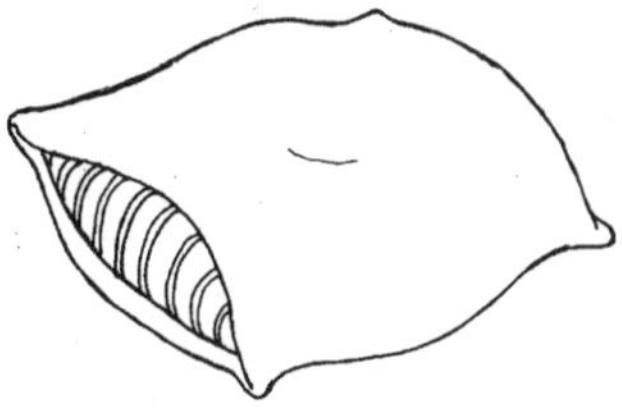

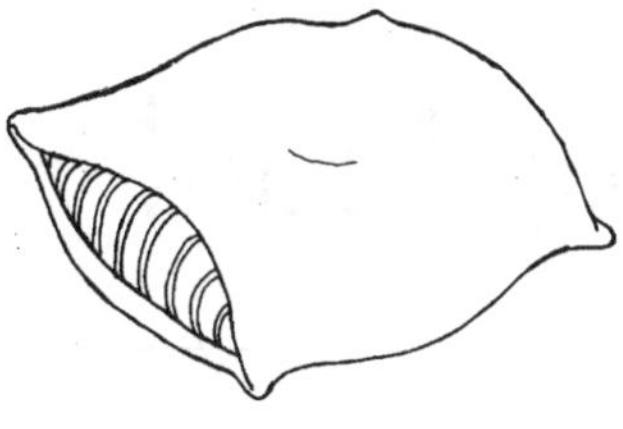

Directions: Help children identify the pictures in each row. Then have them color the pictures that are opposites.

Name ______________________________

Phonics

Blend Words with h

1. hat  

2. mat  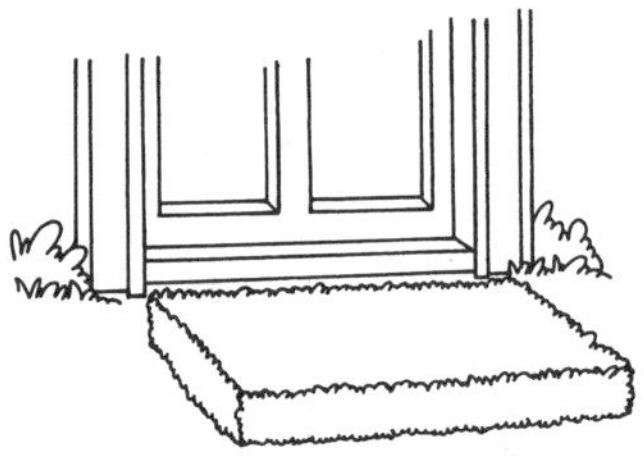

3. ham  

4. cat  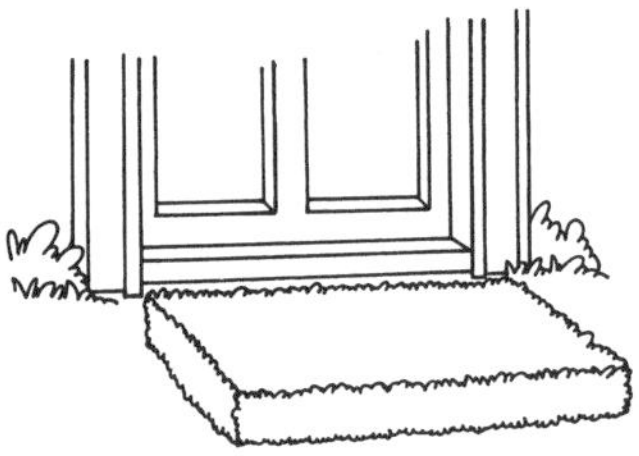

5. pan  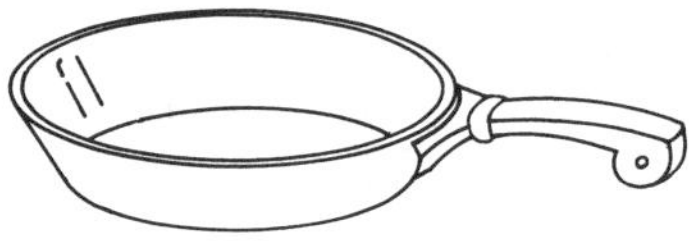

Directions: Have children read each word and circle the picture that matches the word.

ɴame ______________________________

High Frequency Words

Complete Sentences

High Frequency Word
is

1. This is a

______________.

2. Is this a

______________.

3. Look at the

______________.

4. This is a

______________.

irections: Discuss the pictures and name each animal. Have partners take turns completing each sentence orally.

My Book of H h

Hh

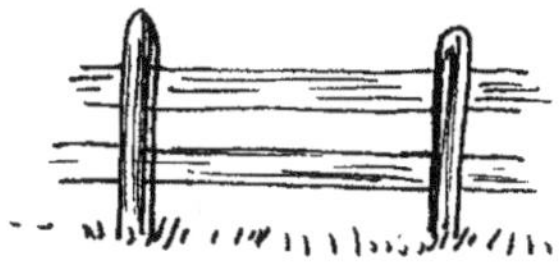

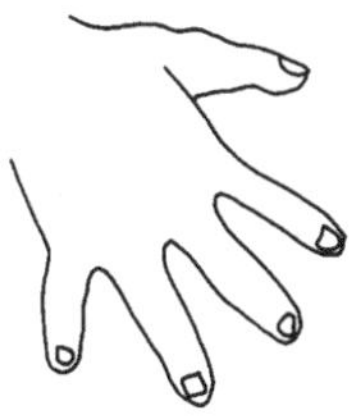
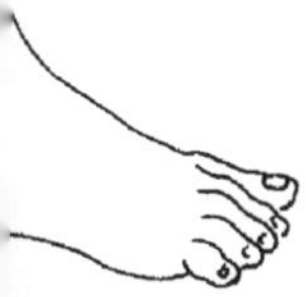

ns: Have children trace the letter forms with a finger as you model letter formation. Then have children name and cut out the cards. em group the cards that start with the sound for *h*, and paste one card on each page. Children can write *Hh* to label their pictures.

Name ____________________

Phonics and High-Frequency Words

Letter and Word Cards

High Frequency Word
is

.	look	I	is
is	this	is	is
his	see	is	is
a	See	is	is

Directions: Duplicate and cut out the word cards for use during practice activities.

Hh

house horse

2

and hello to the hens,

7

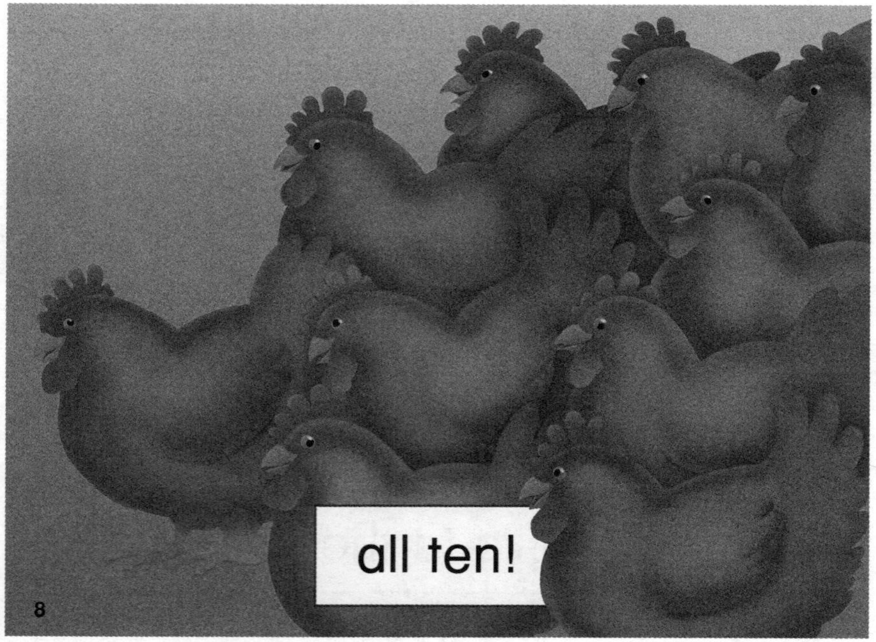

Alphachant™

Hh

by Lada Kratky
illustrated by Jean Hirashima

HAMPTON-BROWN

Hh

hills hen

Name ______________________________

Phonics

Sound for h

1. 	2. 	3. 
4. 	5. 	6. 
7. 	8. 	9. 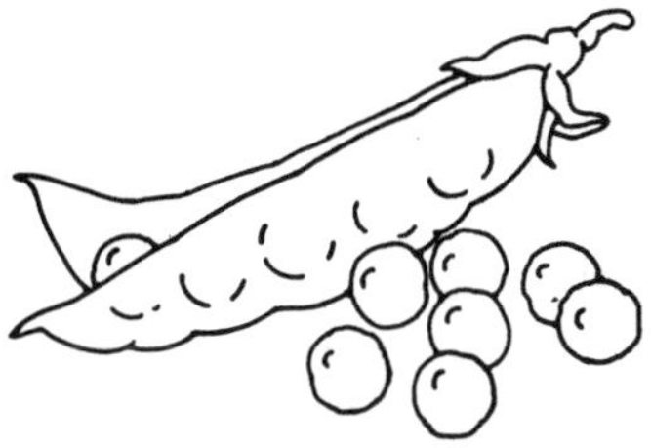

ons: Name each picture with children. Have children color the pictures whose names begin with *h*.

Name ______________________________

Comprehension

Compare Stories

Directions: After discussing ways *The Tale of the Three Little Pigs* and *Honza's Little House* are alike, have children choose one idea to write and/or draw in the oval.

Name ______________________

Phonics and High Frequency Words

Read Sentences

1. See this cat. 

2. Tap this cat. 

3. Look at this can. 

4. Tap this can. 

5. See this cap. 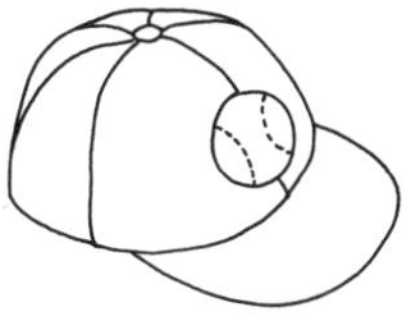

6. Tap this mat. 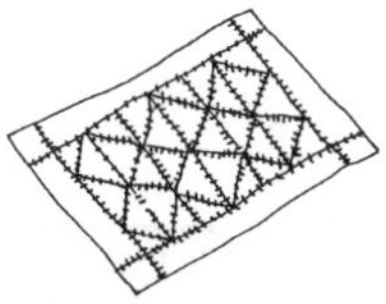

Directions: Discuss the pictures. Have partners read the sentences together and perform the actions.

Name ______________________________

Grammar

Describing Words

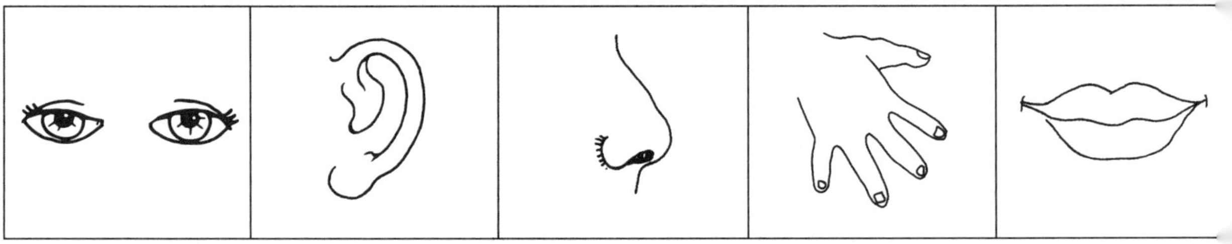

My Favorite Place

Directions: Have each child draw a favorite place. Remind children to include what they see, hear, smell, taste, and/or feel in that place. Ask write and/or dictate at least two describing words that tell about their favorite place. Then have children explain their drawings to the class

Name ______________________

Phonics

Blend Words with n

nap

pat

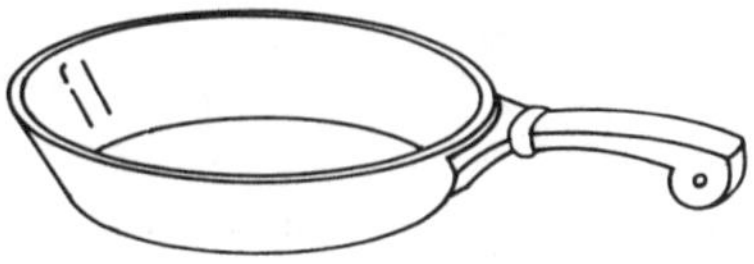

cat

pan

sat

man

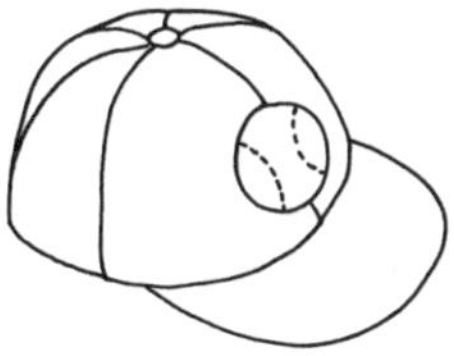

cap

tap

tan

can

cat

nap

Directions: Have children read the words and circle the word that names each picture.

Name ____________________

Comprehension

Setting

Directions: Have children draw a scene from Honza's Little House. Remind them that they should draw the setting with whateve[r] is in the house at that point. Then have partners share and discuss their drawings.

Name ______________________________

High Frequency Words

Read Sentences

High Frequency Word
this

1. Look at this cat.

2. Look at this cat.

3. I can pat this cat.

Directions: Discuss the pictures. Have partners read the sentences together.

My Book of Nn

Nn

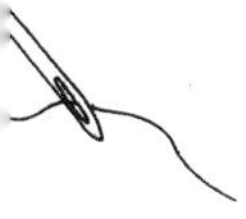

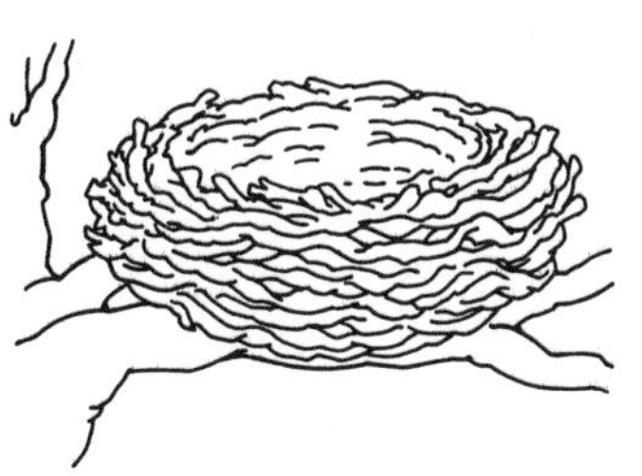

ons: Have children trace the letter forms with a finger as you model letter formation. Then have children name and cut out the cards. em group the cards that start with the sound for *n* and paste one card on each page. Children can write *Nn* to label their pictures.

Name ______________________

High Frequency Words

Word Cards

High Frequency Word
this

a	I
my	look
see	this
the	

Directions: Have children cut out the word cards to use in practice activities. Children can store their words in resealable plastic bags or manila envelopes.

Nn

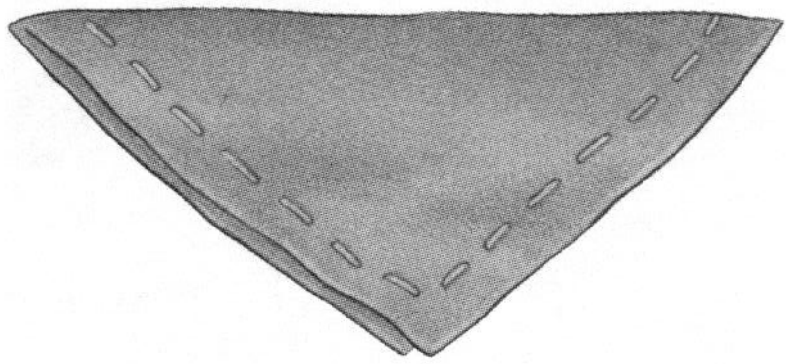

noodles   napkin

Oh no, Nelly!

Let's Chant!

I see noodles on your napkin

noodles on your nose

I see noodles on your toes!

8

Alphachant™

Nn

by Lada Kratky
illustrated by Karen Stormer Brooks

HAMPTON-BROWN

and noodles on your neck

Nn

nose neck

Name ______________________________

Phonics

Sound for n

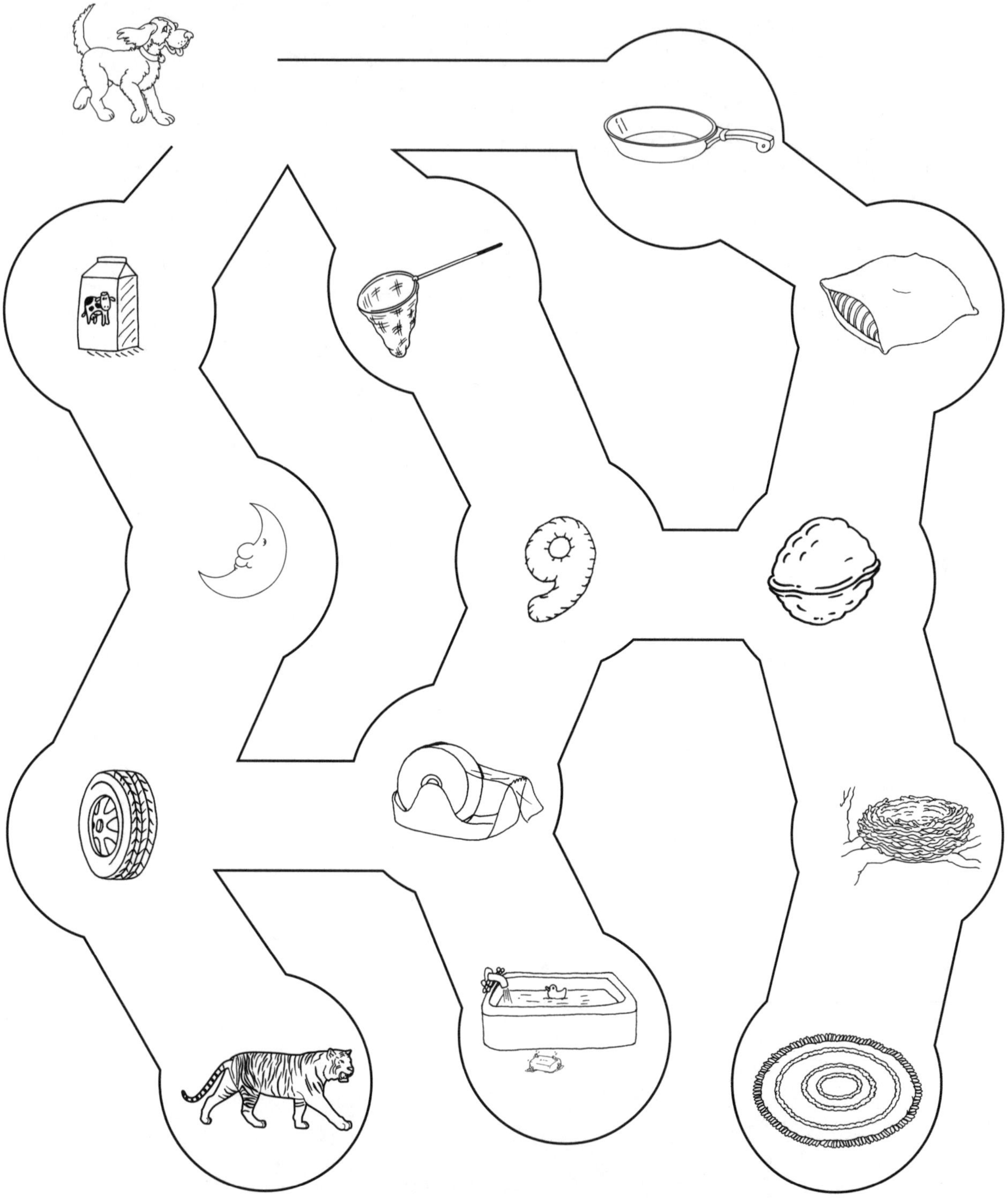

tions: Tell children that the dog's name is Nipper. Name each picture. Have children color the pictures that start with the sound for n. have them draw a line from Nipper to his rug by connecting the colored pictures.

Name ____________________

Comprehension

Little Bat and Tiny Bee

tiny bee

Little Bat

Directions: Talk with children about the ways in which tiny bee and Little Bat are alike. Have children choose one idea to write and/or draw in the oval.

Name ______________________________

Phonics and High Frequency Words

Read Sentences

1. Look at the cat.

2. I pat the cat.

3. Look at the map.

4. I tap the map.

Directions: Discuss the pictures. Have children read the sentences with a partner.

Name ____________________

Grammar

Describing Words

1.

big
little

2.

loud
quiet

3.

slow
fast

Directions: Have children color one animal in each box. Then have them circle a word that describes the animal.

Name ______________________________

Phonics

Blend Words with a

1. cat

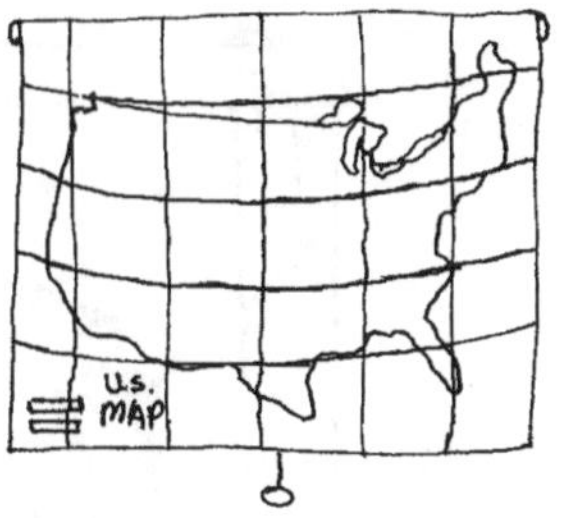

2. map

3. pat

4. cap

5. tap

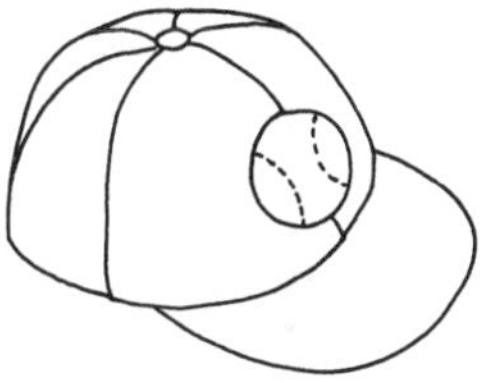

Directions: Have children read each word and draw a line to the picture it matches.

Name ______________________________

Academic Talk

Cut-Outs

Directions: Have children color and cut out the characters, and then glue them to craft sticks. Then have children use the puppets to role-play characters from *There's a Billy Goat in the Garden.*

Name ____________________

Comprehension

Character Map

Directions: Fill out a model map together. Then have children draw, dictate, or write to fill in their own maps.

Name ____________________

High Frequency Words

Read Sentences

High Frequency Word
look

1. Look! I see a  .

2. Look! I see a  .

3. Look! I see a  .

Directions: Discuss the pictures. Have partners read the sentences together.

My Book of Aa

Aa

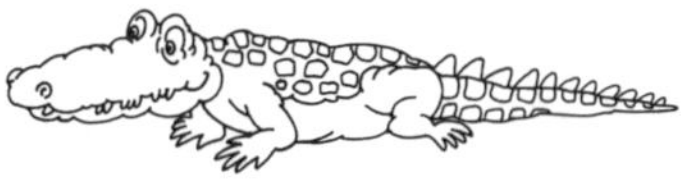

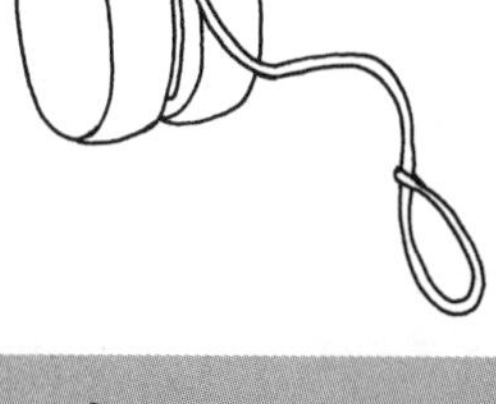

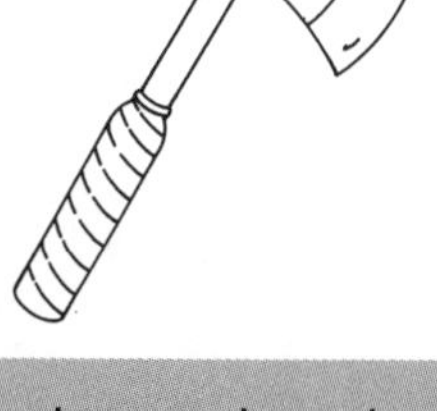

ns: Have children trace the letter forms with a finger as you model letter formation. Then have children name and cut out the cards. m group the cards that start with the sound for *a* and paste one card on each page. Children can write *Aa* to label their pictures.

Name ______________________________

High Frequency Words

Word Cards

High Frequency **Word**
look

at	look
am	I
my	see
a	the

Directions: Have children cut out the word cards to use in practice activities. Children can store their words in resealable plastic bags or manila envelopes.

Aa

ant

anthill

2

and ants on our apple pie.

7

Ants, ants, ants!

Ants on an anthill

Alphachant™

Aa

by Lada Kratky
illustrated by Ken Spengler

HAMPTON-BROWN

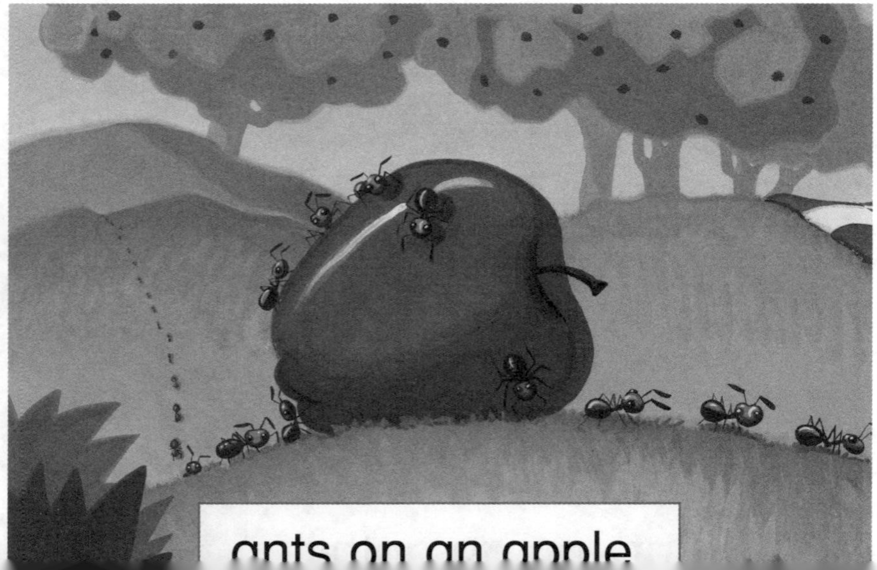

Aa

apple

apple pie

Name ______________________________

Phonics

Sound for a

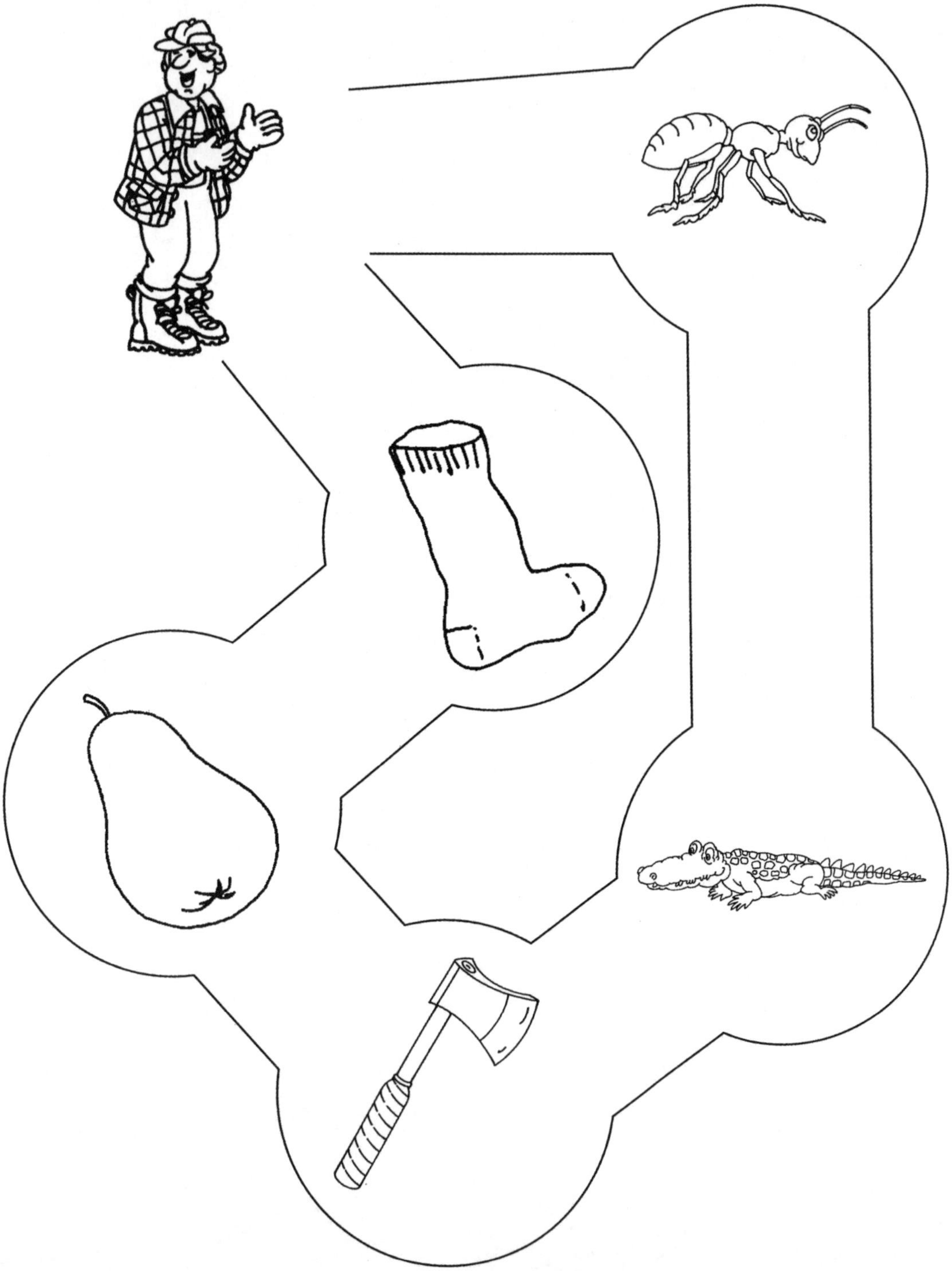

ons: Tell children the man they see is Adam. Then name the other pictures: *ant, sock, pear, alligator, ax.* Ask children to help Adam find
ave them color each picture along the path whose name begins with /ă/ like astronaut, then draw a line to connect the pictures.

Name ______________________________

Comprehension

Compare and Contrast Details

You and Me Together

Goldilocks and the Bear Family

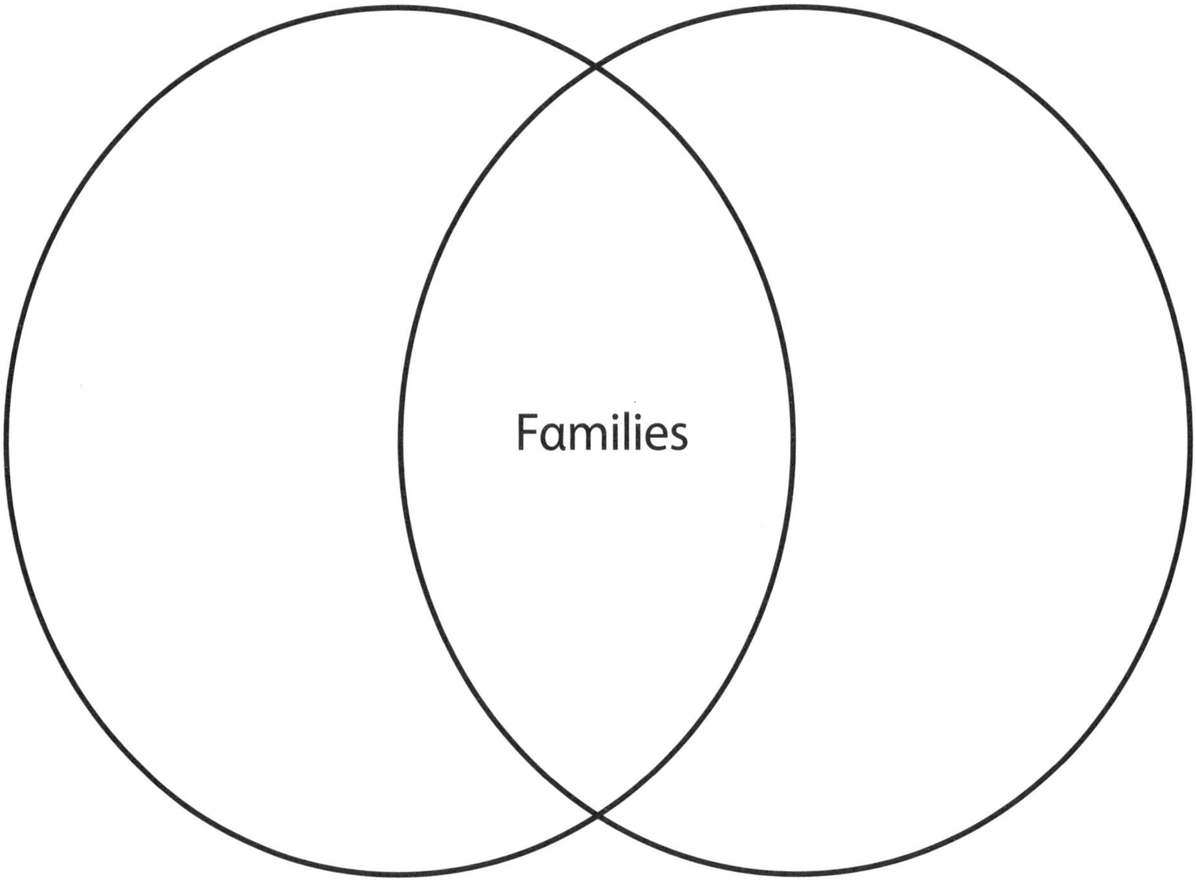

Directions: Read the topic in the center of the Venn diagram. Have children draw or write about a family from *You and Me Together* in the left circle. Have them draw or write about the Bear family in the right circle. Possible responses are shown.

Name ______________________________

Phonics and High Frequency Words

Read Sentences

High Frequency Word
I

☐ 1. I see a  .

☐ 2. I see the  .

☐ 3. I see the  .

☐ 4. I see a  .

☐ 5. I see a  .

☐ 6. I see the  .

☐ 7. I see the 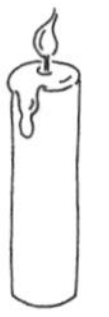 .

☐ 8. I see the  .

☐ 9. I see the 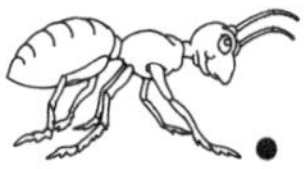 .

☐ 10. I see a 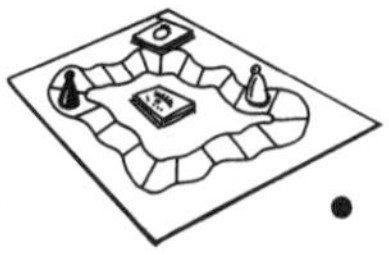 .

Directions: Name each picture with children. Then have partners take turns reading each sentence. Ask children to color the pictures whose names begin with the sound for *c*. Then have them check off items that they would like at a birthday party.

Name ____________________

Grammar

Pronouns

Directions: Make enough cards for partners or small groups to each have a set. Cut apart the cards and paste on index cards if necessary. Use the cards as described on TE page T150.

Name ______________________

Phonics

Sound for Cc

1.  c	2. 	3. 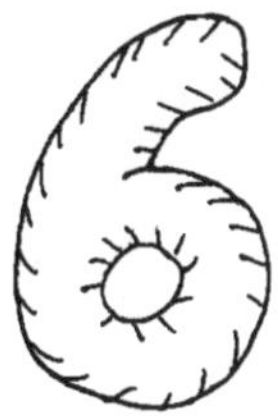
4. 	5. 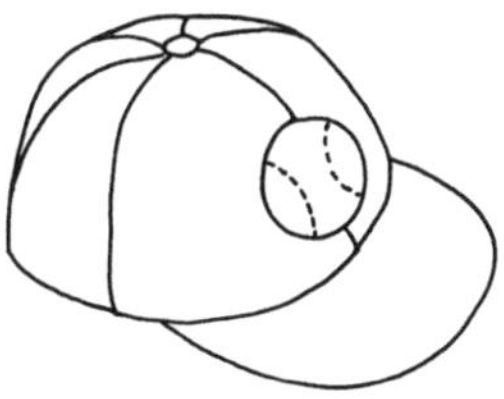	6. 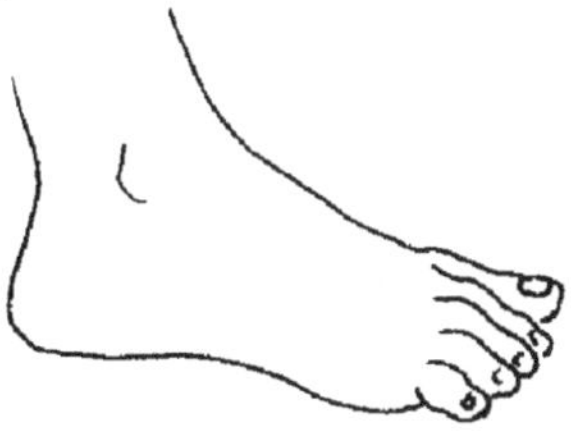
7. 	8. 	9. 

ons: Name each picture with children. Have children decide if the word begins with the sound for the letter *c*. Ask them to write *c* if
'd begins with the sound for *c*. Have them leave the line blank if the word doesn't begin with the sound for *c*.

Name ______________________________

Comprehension

Identify Details

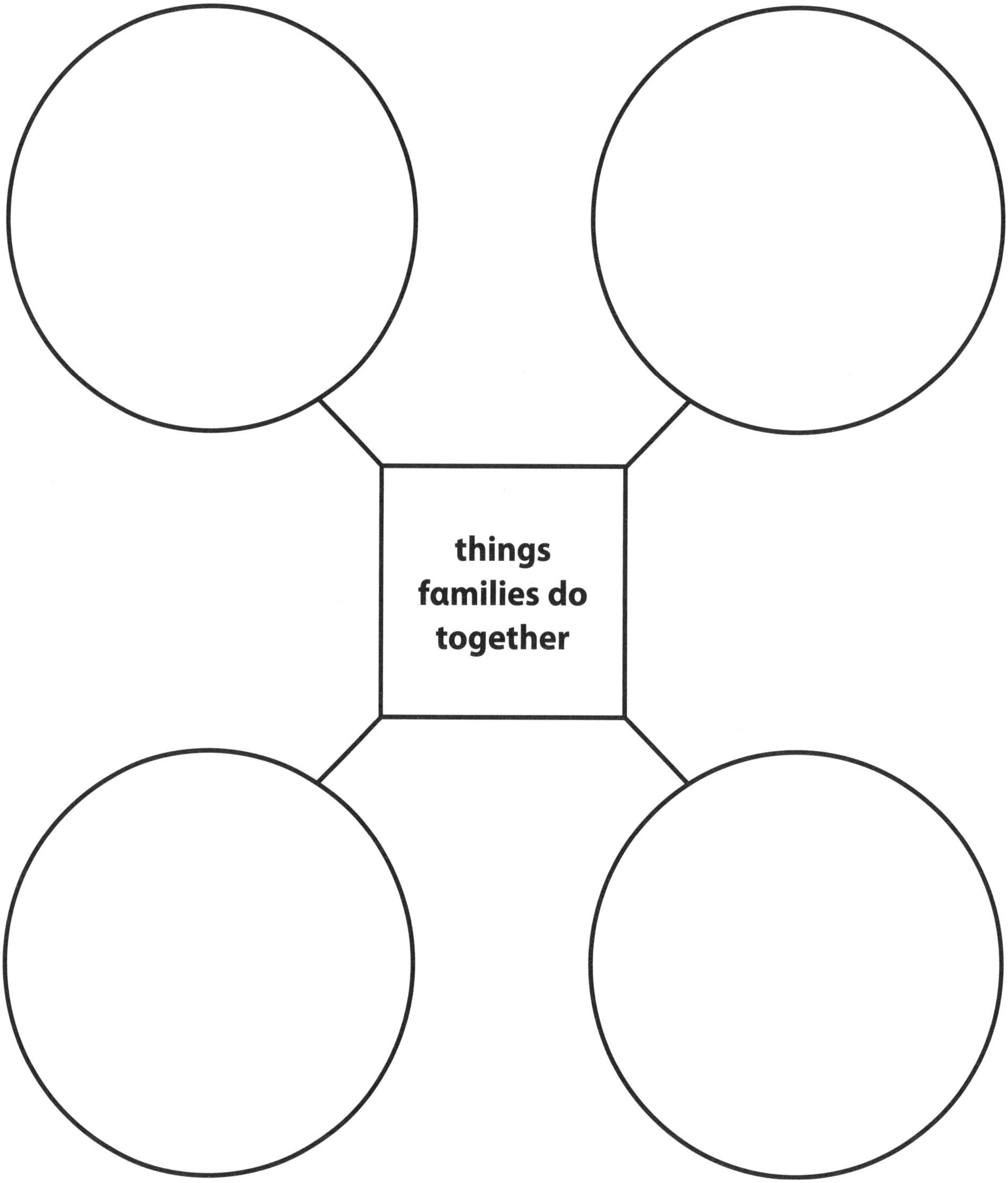

Directions: Remind children that the topic of *You and Me Together* is "families." Read the main idea in the center of the idea web. Have each child draw or write one detail from the book in each circle.

Name ______________________________

High Frequency Words

Read Sentences

1.

___ see a cape.

2.

___ see a carrot.

3.

___ see a camel.

4.

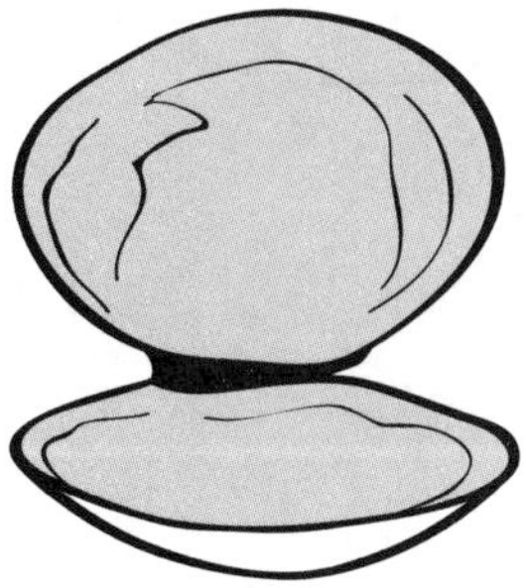

___ see a clam.

5.

___ see a cage.

6.

___ see a cub.

Directions: Name each picture with children. Ask what letter all of the picture names begin with. (c) Then have children write the word / to complete each sentence. Ask partners to take turns reading the sentences out loud.

My Book of C c

Cc

ions: Have children trace the letter forms with a finger as you model letter formation. Then have children name and cut out the cards.
hem group the cards that start with the sound for *c* and paste one card on each page. Children can write *Cc* to label their pictures.

Name ______________________

Phonics and High-Frequency Words

Letter and Word Cards

High Frequency **Word**
I

Cc	a	my	I
Cc	Cc	See	I
Cc	Cc	the	I
Cc	Cc	see	I

Directions: Duplicate and cut out letter and word cards. Children will need one of each card for use during practice activities.

Cc

car cow

Cat's car is fastest,

Let's Chant!

There go the cars!

Cow's car is fast

but Caterpillar wins!

Camel's car is faster

Alphachant™

Cc

by Lada Kratky
illustrated by Eldon Doty

HAMPTON-BROWN

Cc

camel

cat

Name ________________________________

Phonics

Sound for Cc

C c	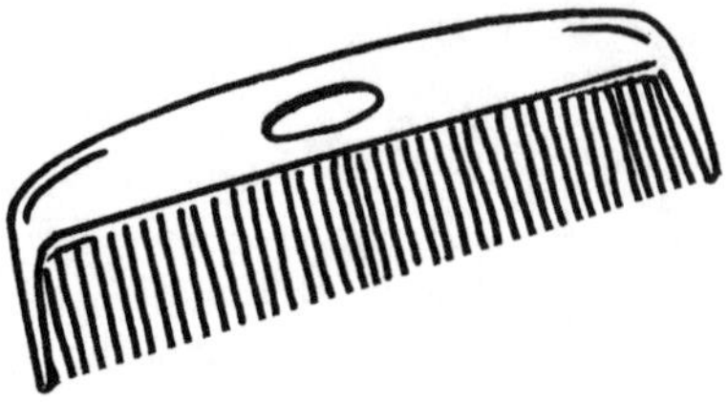	
	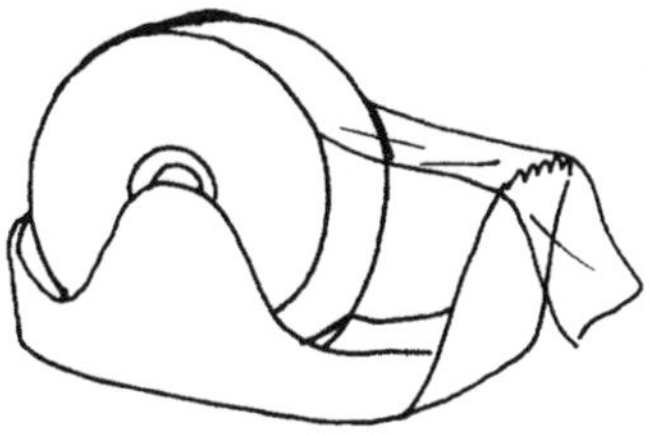	
	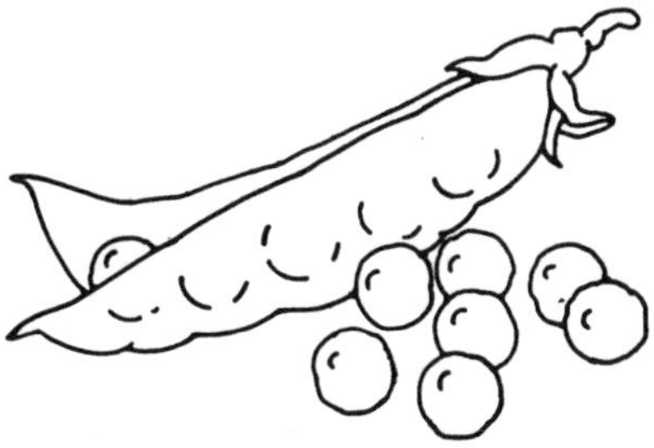	

ections: Name the letter and each picture with children. Have children cut out the cards. Ask partners to sort by beginning sound, uping the pictures whose names begin with the sound for *c* with the *Cc* card. Have partners name all of the pictures in the *Cc* group.

Name ______________________

Comprehension

Compare Stories

Directions: After comparing *The Donut* and *Feast for 10,* have children draw and write about one way the stories are alike.

Name ________________________________

Phonics and High Frequency Words

Read Sentences

1. See the 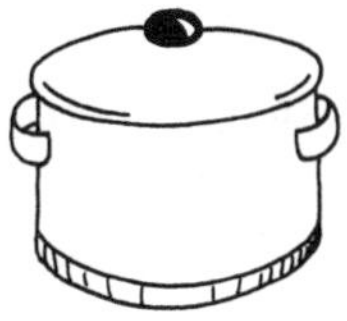 .

2. See the 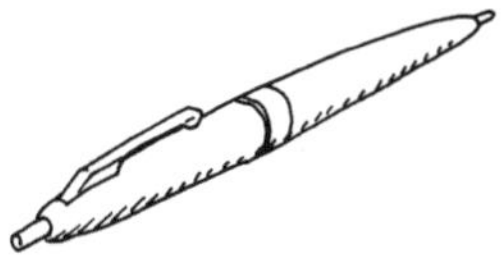 .

3. See a  .

4. See the  .

5. See my  .

6. See the  .

Directions: Name each picture with children. Ask what letter all of the picture names begin with. *(p)* Then have partners take turns reading the sentences out loud.

Name

Grammar

Plural Nouns

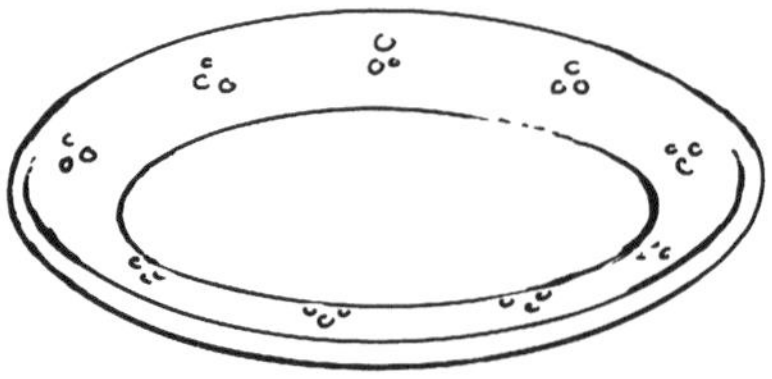

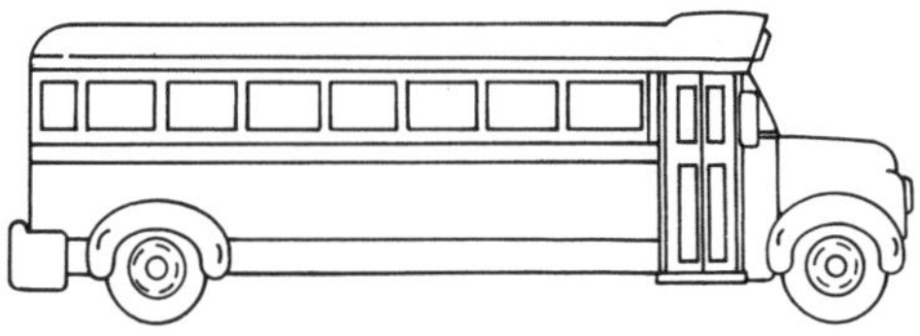

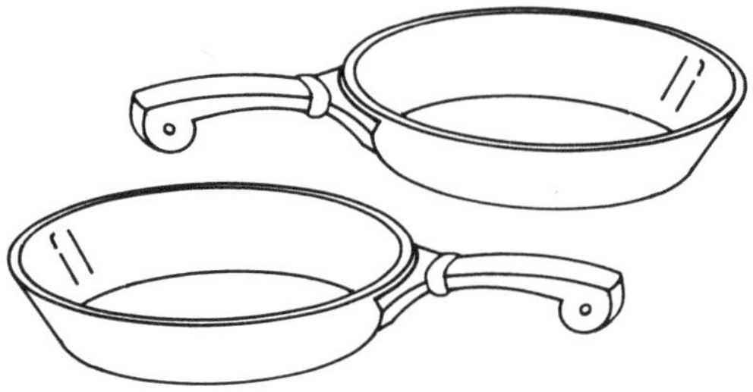

Directions: Have children look at each picture, name it, and tell if it shows one or more than one. Then have them color the pictures that show more than one. When they have finished, have children name the pictures with a partner.

Name ____________________

Phonics

Sound for Pp

1. 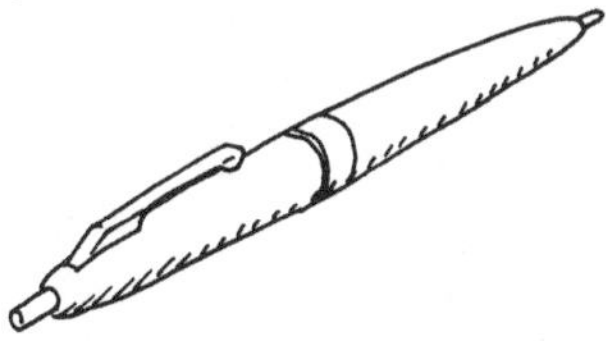 p	2. 	3. 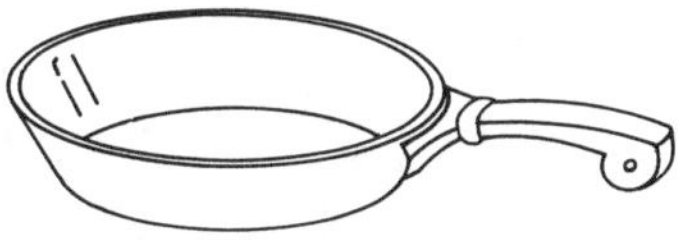
4. 	5. 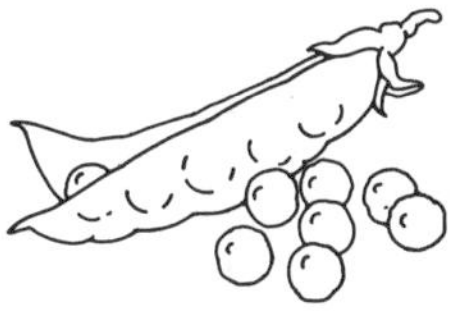	6. 
7. 	8. 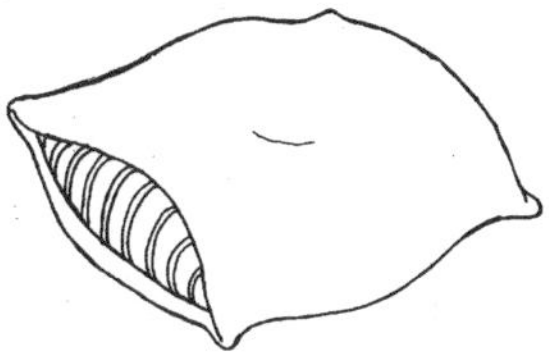	9. 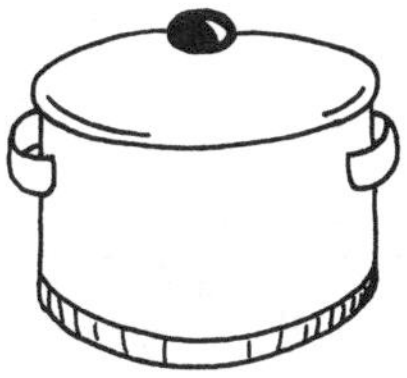

irections: Name each picture with children. Have children decide if the word begins with the letter *p*. Ask them to write *p* the word begins with *p*. Have them leave the line blank if the word doesn't begin with *p*.

Name ______________________________

Comprehension

Sequence Chain

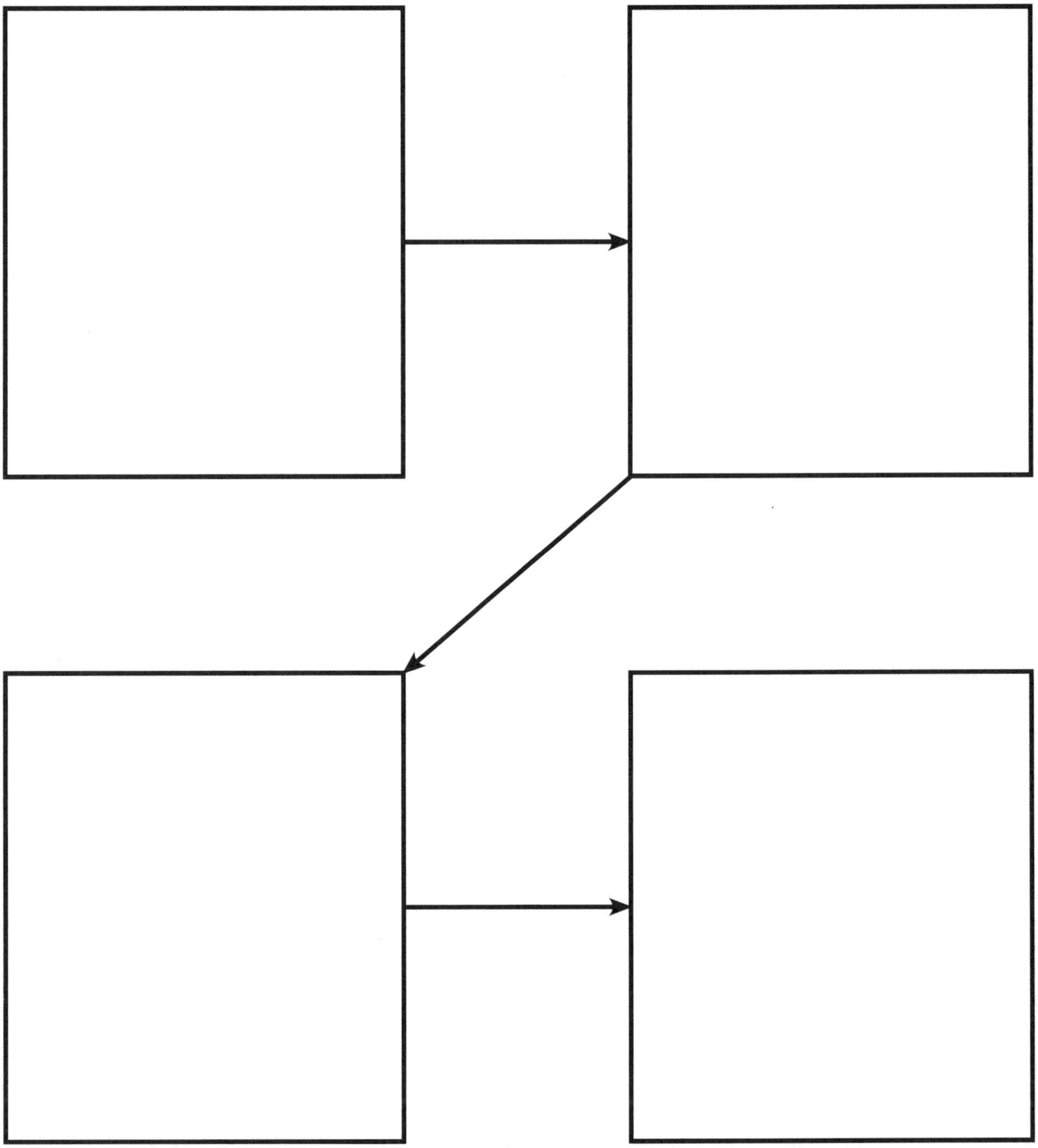

Directions: Have children draw pictures to show the order in which things happen in *Feast for 10*. Point out the arrows that show how to draw the events in the correct order.

Name ______________________

High Frequency Words

Read Sentences

High Frequency Word
the

1. See the ________.	2. See the ________.
3. See the ________.	4. See the ________.

Directions: Have children complete each sentence frame by drawing a food they like. Have partners share their pictures and read their sentences.

My Book of P p

P p

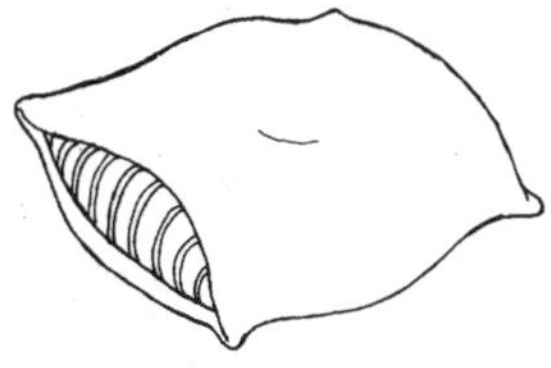

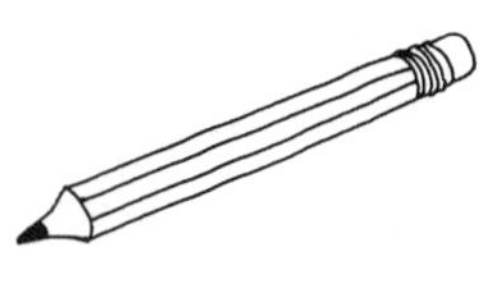
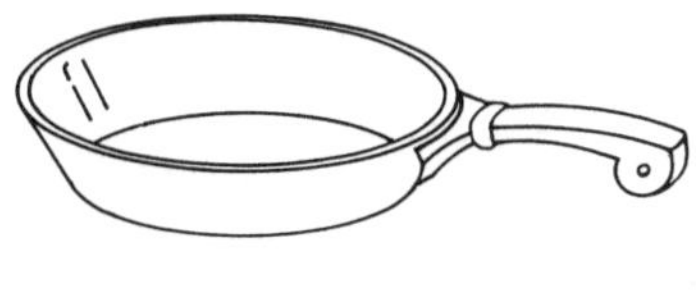

ns: Have children trace the letter forms with a finger as you model letter formation. Then have children name and cut out the cards. m group the cards that start with the sound for *p* and paste one card on each page. Children can write *Pp* to label their pictures.

Name ______________________________

Phonics and High-Frequency Words

Letter and Word Cards

High Frequency Word
the

Pp	Pp	a	the
Pp	Pp	my	the
Pp	Pp	See	the
Pp	Pp	the	the

Directions: Duplicate and cut out letter and word cards. Children will need one of each card for use during practice activities.

Pp

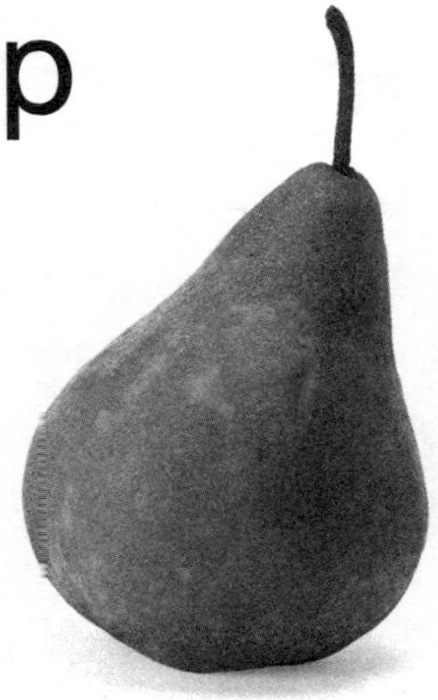

pear peach

2

and pass the peas.

7

Let's Chant!

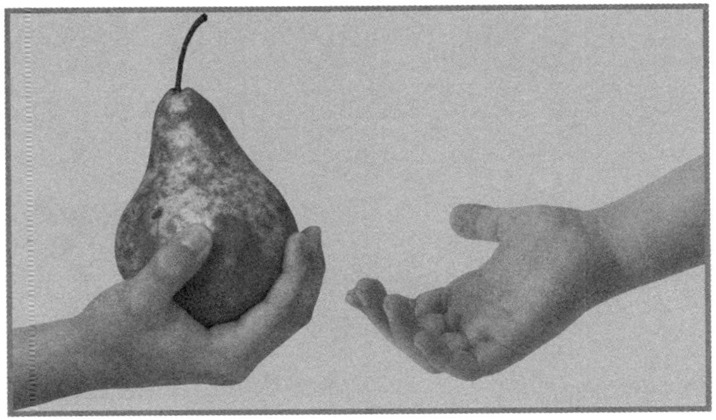

Pass the pear

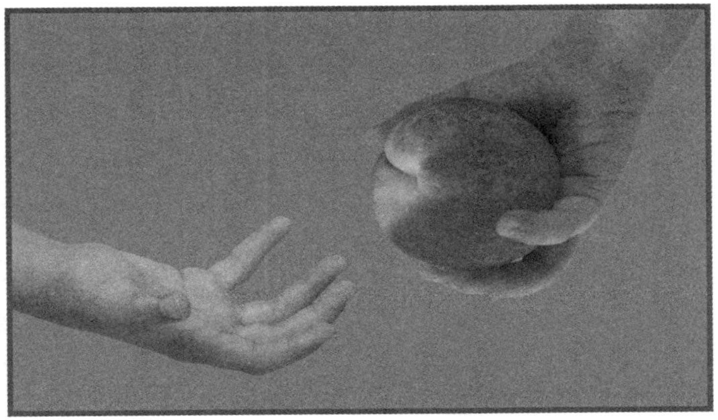

Pass the peach

Please!

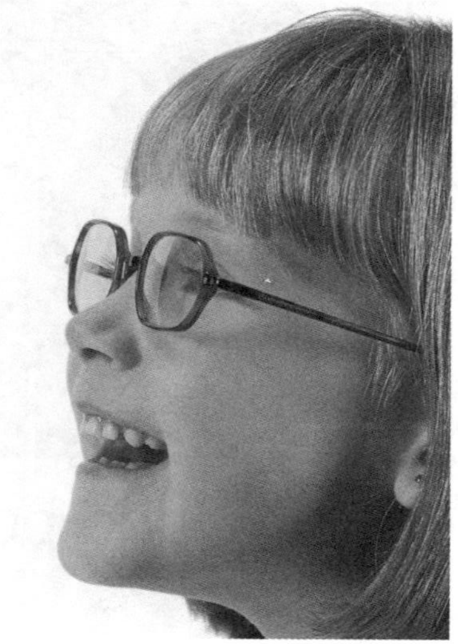

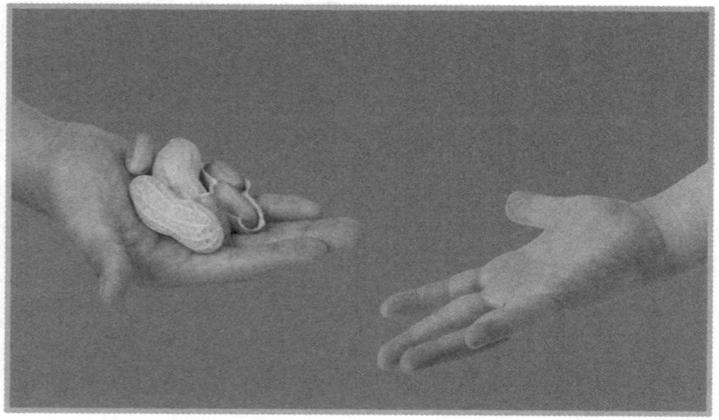

Pass the peanuts

Alphachant™

Pp

by Lada Kratky
photographed by Clem Spalding

HAMPTON-BROWN

Pp

peanuts peas

Name ______________________________

Phonics

Sound for Pp

P p	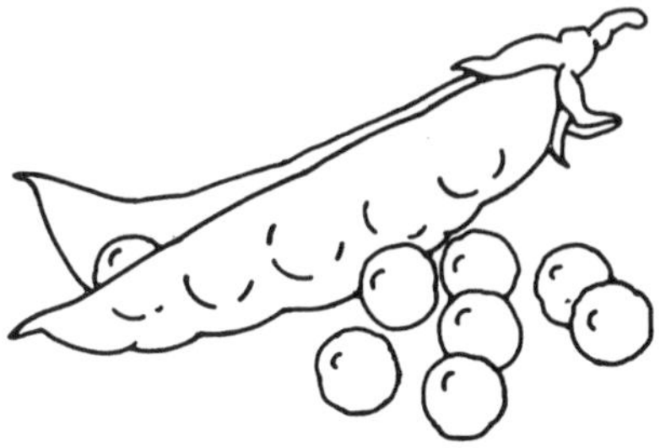	
		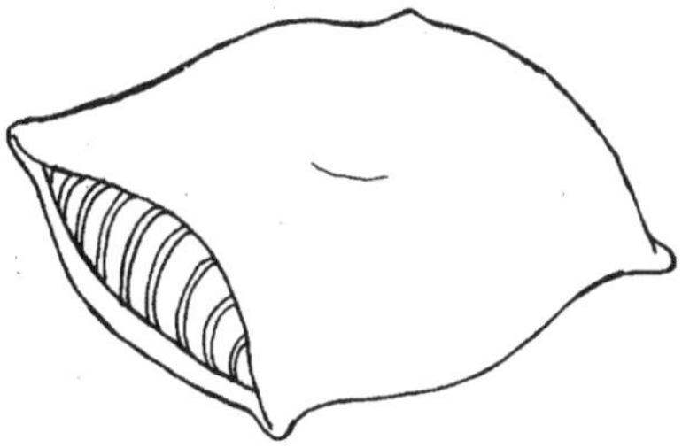
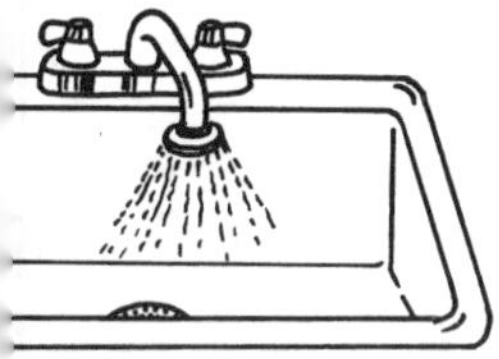		

ns: Name the letter and each picture with children. Have children cut out the cards. Ask partners to sort by beginning sound, the pictures whose names begin with the sound for *p* with the *Pp* card. Have partners name all of the pictures in the *Pp* group.

Name ____________________

Comprehension

Compare Predictions

Directions: After comparing predictions they made about the week's reading, have children draw and write about one prediction they made. Prompt them by asking, *What did you predict?*

Name ______________________________

Phonics and High Frequency Words

Write Sentences

1.

See a top.

2.

________ a tractor.

3.

________ a tire.

4.

________ twins.

5.

________ a truck.

6.

________ a turkey.

Directions: Name each picture with children. Ask what letter all of the picture names begin with. (t) Then have children write the word *See* to complete each sentence. Ask partners to take turns reading the sentences out loud.

Name ______________________________

Grammar

Nouns

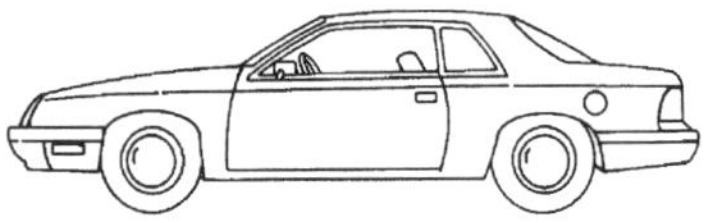

Directions: Have children color all the pictures of people green. Have children color all of the pictures of places red. Have children color all of the things blue.

Name ______________________________

Phonics

Sound for <u>Tt</u>

1.

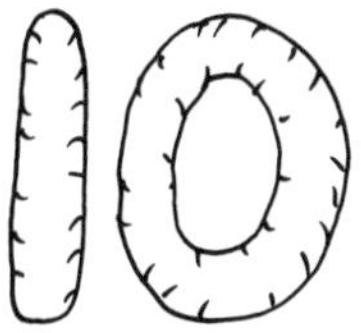

t

2.

3.

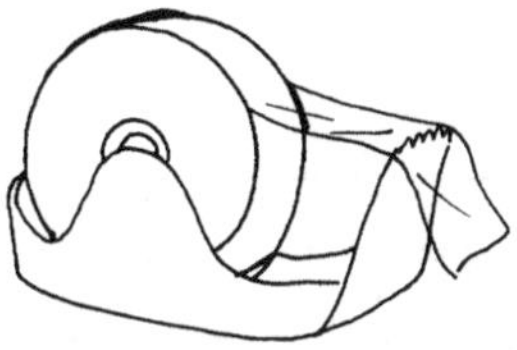

4.

5.

6.

7.

8.

9.

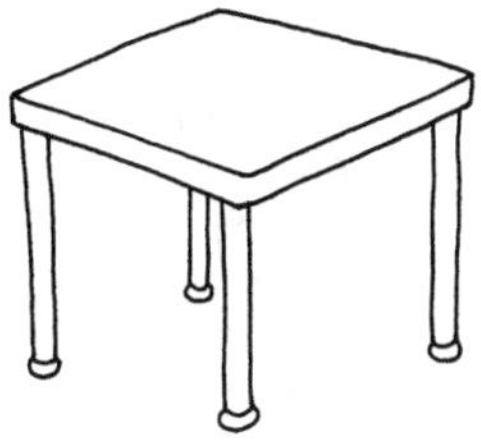

Directions: Name each picture with children. Have children decide if the word begins with the letter *t*. Ask them to write *t* if the word begins with *t*. Have them leave the line blank if the word doesn't begin with *t*.

Name ______________________________

Comprehension

Make Predictions

The Snowy Day

Directions: Read the book title aloud. Then have children draw a picture of what they think the book will be about. Prompt them by asking, *What will the story be about?*

Name ____________________

High Frequency Words

Read Sentences

High Frequency Word
see

1. See my ________.	2. See my ________.
3. See my ________.	4. See my ________.

Directions: Have children complete each sentence frame by drawing something they have at home. Have partners share their pictures and read their sentences.

My Book of T t

Tt

ions: Have children trace the letter forms with a finger as you model letter formation. Then have children name and cut out the cards. hem group the cards that start with the sound for *t,* and paste one card on each page. Children can write *Tt* to label their pictures.

Name ______________________________

Phonics and High-Frequency Words

Letter and Word Cards

High Frequency Word
see

Tt	Tt	a	see
Tt	Tt	my	see
Tt	Tt	See	see
Tt	Tt	See	see

Directions: Duplicate and cut out letter and word cards. Children will need one of each card for use during practice activities.

Tt

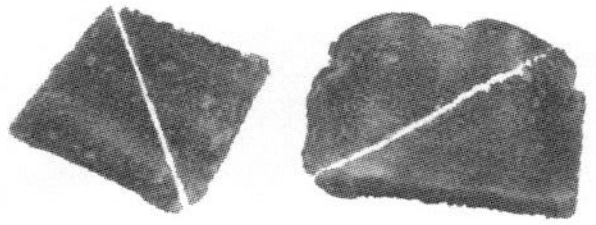

table toast

and tea and toast for me.

Let's Chant!

I'll set the table for tea.

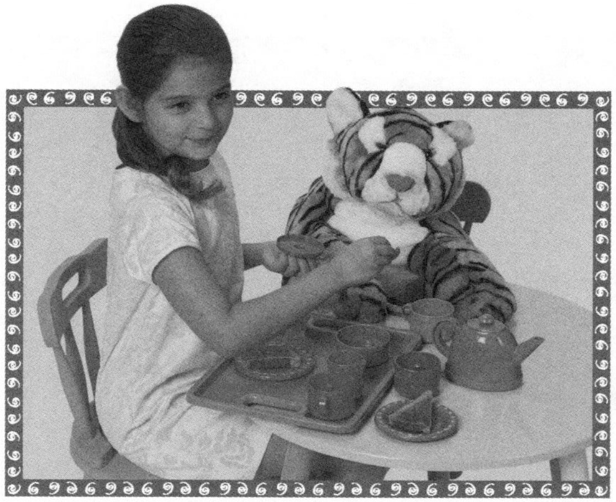

Tea and toast for Tiger.

Tea and toast for three!

8

Alphachant™

Tt

by Lada Kratky
photographed by Clem Spalding

HAMPTON-BROWN

tea and toast for Turtle,

Tt

tiger turtle

Name ____________________

Phonics

Sound for Tt

T t

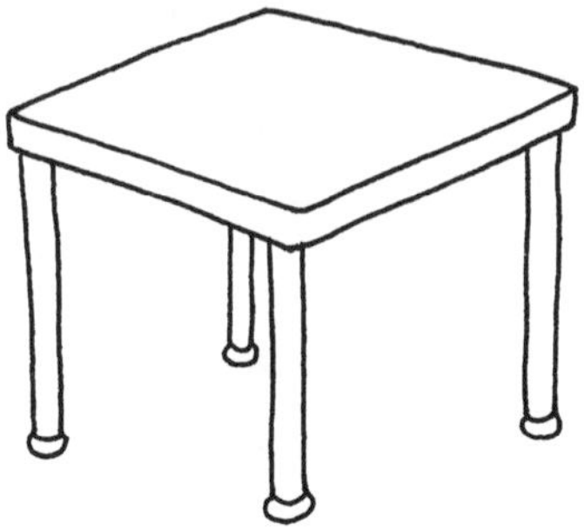

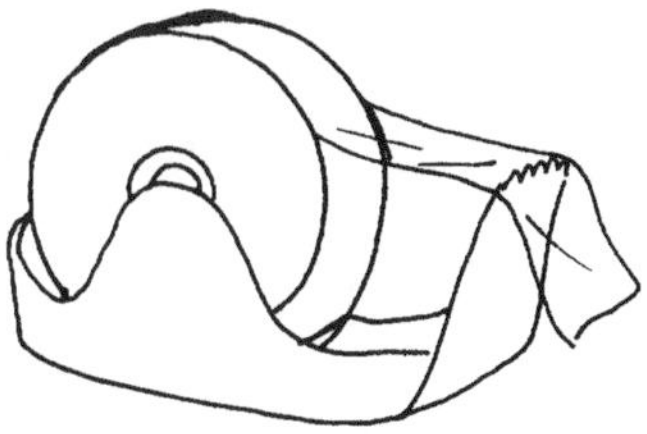

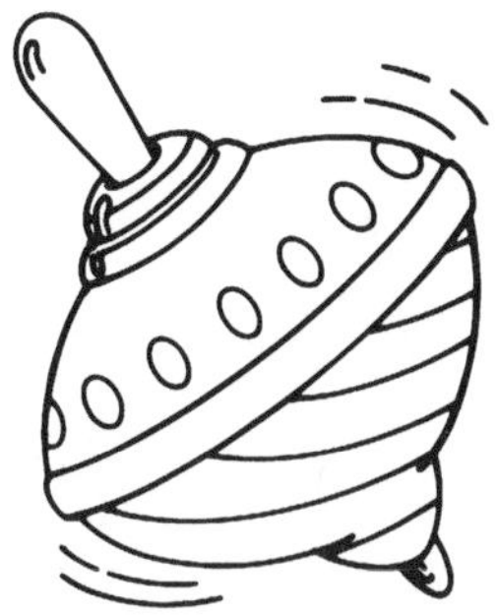

ions: Name the letter and each picture with children. Have children cut out the cards. Ask partners to sort by beginning sound, g the pictures whose names begin with the sound for *t* with the *Tt* card. Then have partners name all of the pictures in the *Tt* group.

Name ______________________________

Comprehension

Compare Texts

Directions: Have children draw or write about the topic of *Gio and His Family* in the top left box. Have them draw or write about the *A Tasty Treat!* in the top right box. Discuss ways that the two selections are alike. Have children draw one idea in the lower box.

Name ____________________

Phonics and High Frequency Words

Write Labels

1.

my

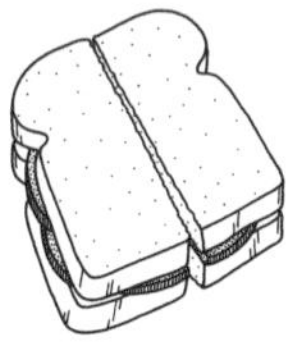

2.

3.

4.

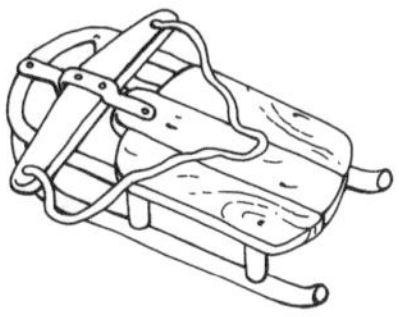

5.

6.

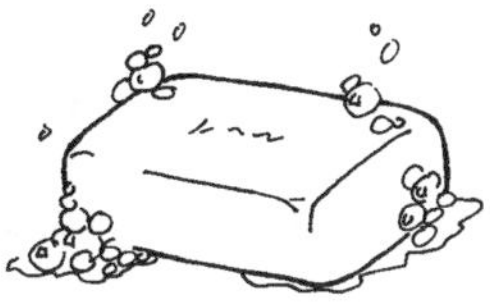

Directions: Name each picture with children. Ask what letter all of the picture names begin with. (s) Then have children write the word my or a to complete each label. Ask partners to take turns reading the labels out loud.

Name ______________________

Grammar

Nouns

ons: Have partners cut out the pictures. Then have them sort the pictures placing people words in one pile, thing words in a second, ce words in a third. Finally, have children take turns choosing two cards from different piles and using the words in an oral sentence.

Name ______________________

Phonics

Sound for Ss

1\. 

S

2\. 

3\. 

4\. 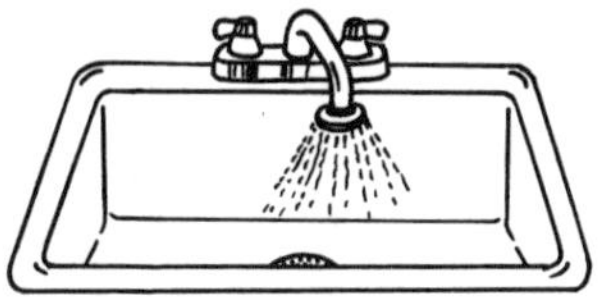

5\. 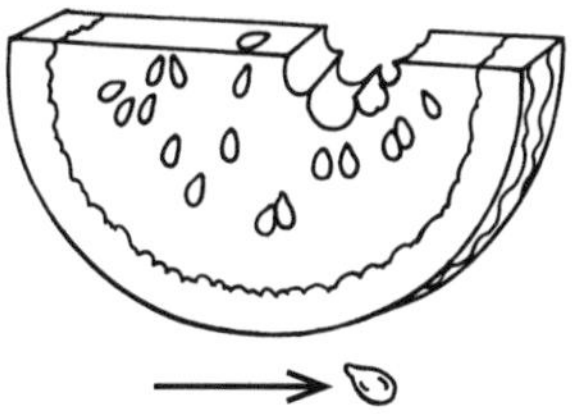

6\. 

7\. 

8\. 

9\. 

Directions: Name each picture with children. Have children decide if the word begins with the letter s. Ask them to write s if the word begins with s. Have them leave the line blank if the word doesn't begin with s.

Name ______________________

Comprehension

Identify Topic and Main Ideas

Directions: Have each child draw or write the topic of *Gio and His Family* in the center oval. Then have them draw or write four main ideas from the story in the surrounding boxes.

Name ____________________

High Frequency Words

Read Labels

High Frequency **Word**
my

☐ **1.** my

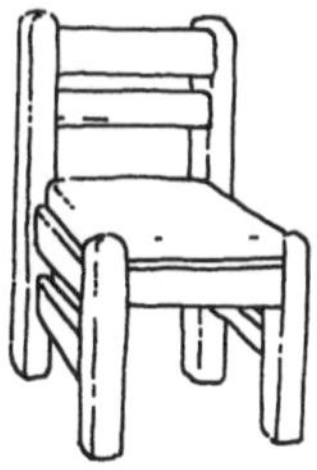

☐ **2.** my

☐ **3.** my

☐ **4.** my

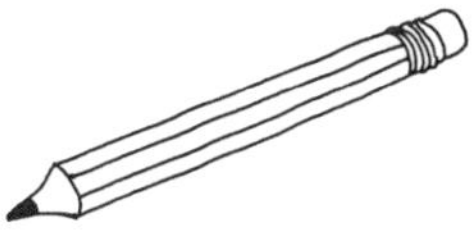

☐ **5.** my

☐ **6.** my

☐ **7.** my

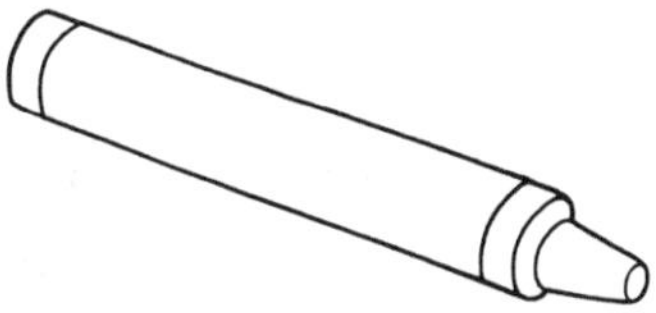

☐ **8.** my

☐ **9.** my

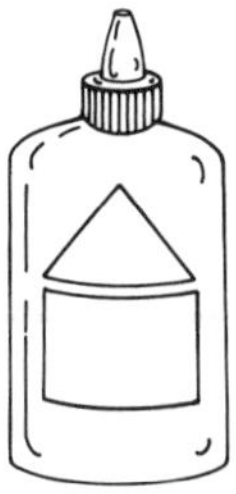

☐ **10.** my

Directions: Name each picture with children. Then have partners take turns reading each label. Ask children to check off items on the list that they have or use at school.

My Book of S s

S s

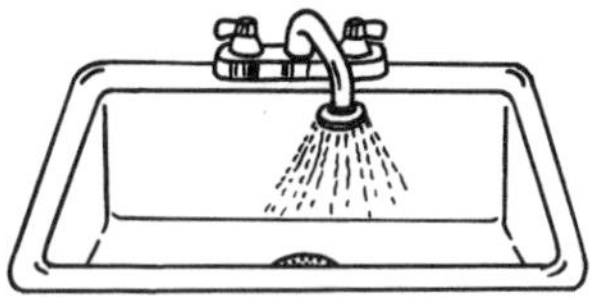

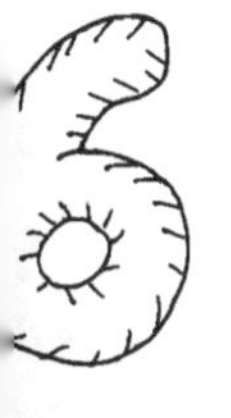

ons: Have children trace the letter forms with a finger as you model letter formation. Then have children name and cut out the cards.
em group the cards that start with the sound for *s* and paste one card on each page. Children can write *Ss* to label their pictures.

Name ____________________

Phonics and High Frequency Words

Letter and Word Cards

High Frequency Word
my

s	S s	a	my
s	S s	my	my
s	S s	my	my
s	S s	my	my

Directions: Duplicate and cut out letter and word cards for use during practice activities.

Ss

socks sand

My socks are in the sun.

Let's Chant!

See my socks!

My socks are in the sand

My socks are lots of fun!

Alphachant™

Ss

by Lada Kratky
photographed by John Paul Endress

HAMPTON-BROWN

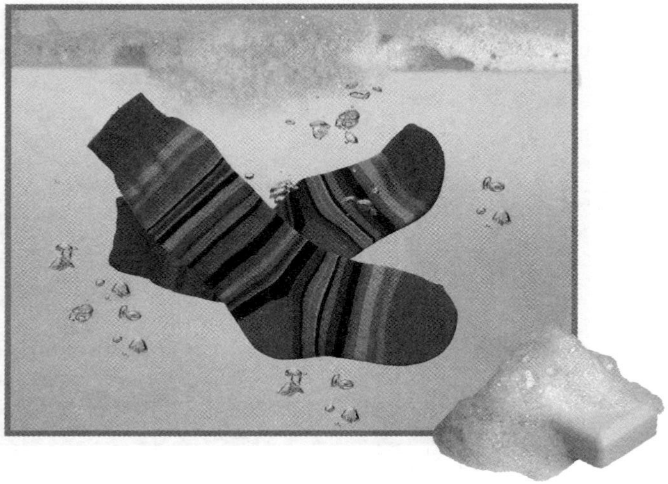

My socks are in the soap

Ss

soap sun

Name ____________________

Phonics

Sound for Ss

Ss

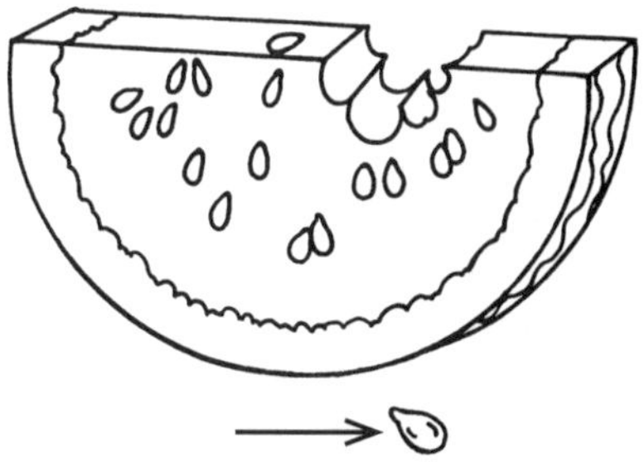

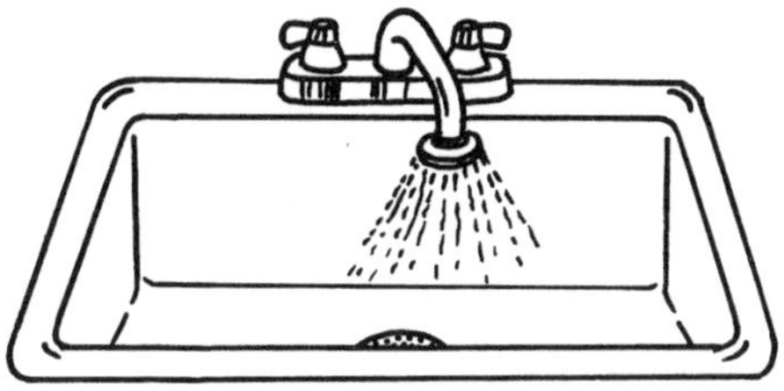

Directions: Name the letters and each picture with children. Have children cut out the cards. Ask partners to sort by beginning sound. After they have finished sorting, have partners name all of the pictures in the *Ss* group.

Name ______________________________

Comprehension

Sequence Chart

Morning	Noon	Afternoon

Directions: Have children draw something children in the songs do in the morning, at noon, and in the afternoon. Have them tell a partner about their drawings.

Name ____________________

Phonics and High Frequency Words

Write Labels

1.

2.

3.

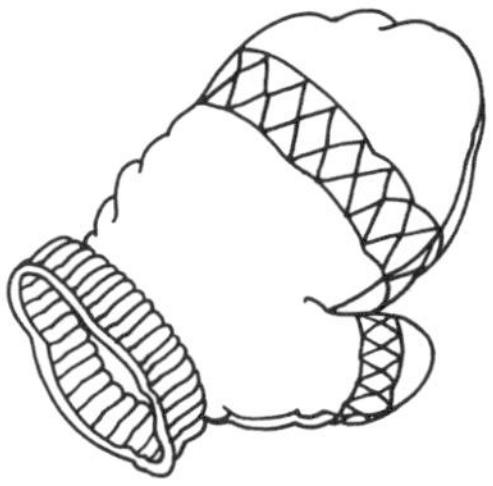

4.

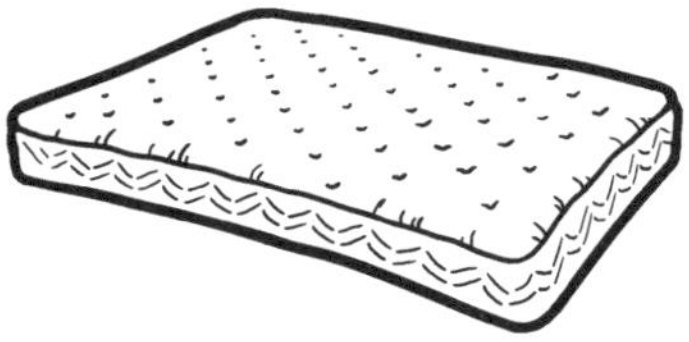

5.

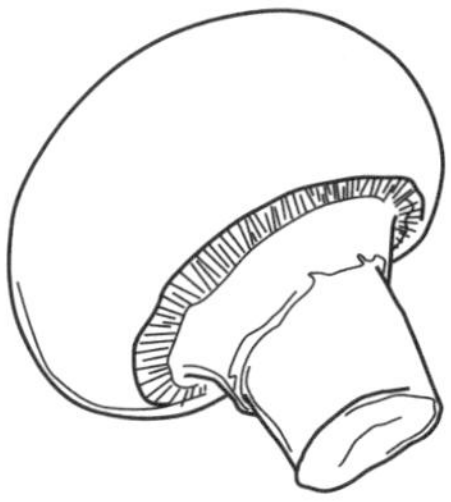

6.

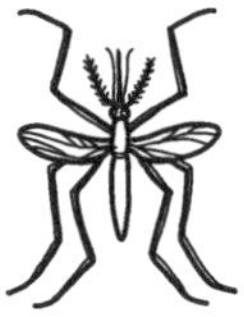

Directions: Name each picture with children. Ask what letter all of the picture names begin with. (m) Then have children write the word *a* to complete each label. Ask partners to take turns reading the labels out loud.

Name ______________________

Phonics

Sound for m

1. 	2. 	3. 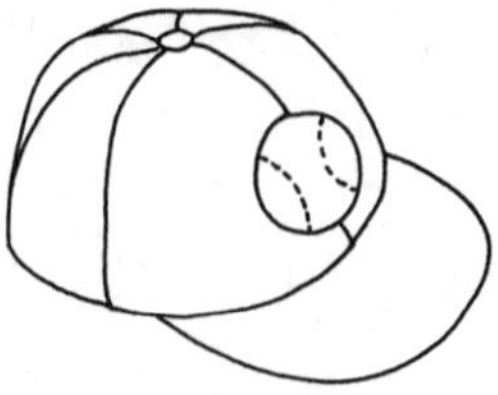
4. 	5. 	6. 
7. 	8. 	9. 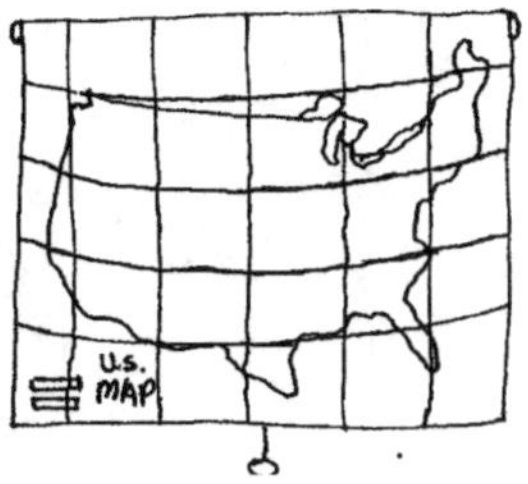

Directions: Name each picture with children. Have children decide if the word begins with the letter *m*. Ask them to write *m* if the word begins with *m*. Have them leave the line blank if the word doesn't begin with *m*.

Name ______________________________

Comprehension

Sequence Chart

Beginning	Middle	End

Directions: Have children draw one thing that happens at the beginning, in the middle, and at the end of a story they know. Have them tell a partner about their drawings.

Name ______________________

High Frequency Words

Read Labels

High Frequency Word
a

☐ **1.** a

☐ **2.** a

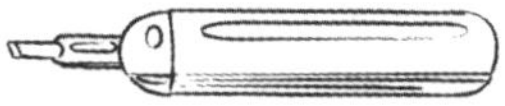

☐ **3.** a

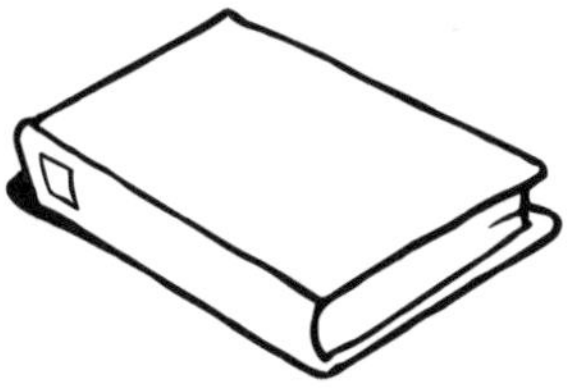

☐ **4.** a

☐ **5.** a

☐ **6.** a

☐ **7.** a

☐ **8.** a

☐ **9.** a

☐ **10.** a

Directions: Name each picture with children. Then have partners take turns reading each label. Ask partners to look for the items on the list in the classroom. Have them check off the items they are able to find.

My Book of Mm

Mm

Directions: Have children trace the letter forms with a finger as you model letter formation. Then have children name and cut out the cards. Have them group the cards that start with the sound for m, and paste one card on each page. Children can write Mm to label their pictures.

Name ______________________________

Phonics and High Frequency Words

Letter and Word Cards

High Frequency Word
a

Mm	Mm	a	a
Mm	Mm	a	a
Mm	Mm	a	a
Mm	Mm	a	a

Directions: Duplicate and cut out letter and word cards. Children will need one of each card for use during practice activities.

Mm

mom macaroni

My mom makes lunch

Milk, mmm.

Macaroni, mmm

More, more. Mmm!

8

8

Alphachant™

Mm

by Lada Kratky
illustrated by Mike Reed

HAMPTON-BROWN

1

Melon, mmm

Mm

melon

milk

Name ______________________________

Phonics

Sound for m

m	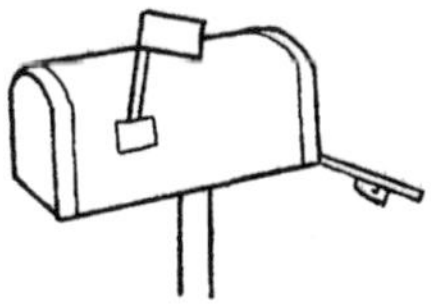	

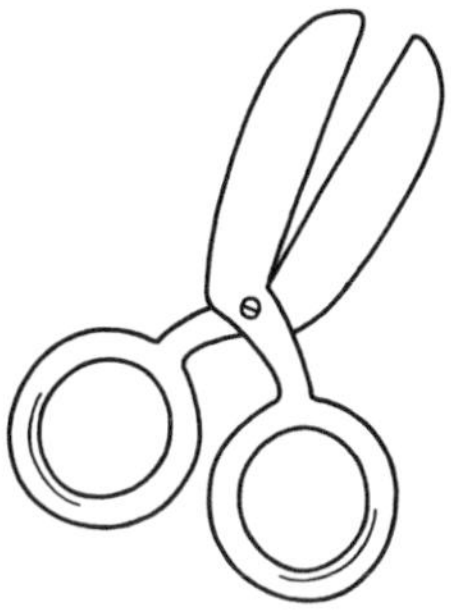		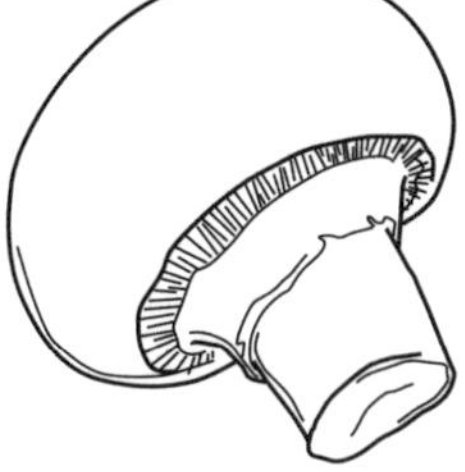

tions: Name the letter and each picture with children. Have children cut out the cards. Ask partners to group the pictures whose names with the sound for *m*. After they have finished sorting, have partners name all of the pictures in the *Mm* group.

Name ______________________________

Phonics

Sound for m

1

2

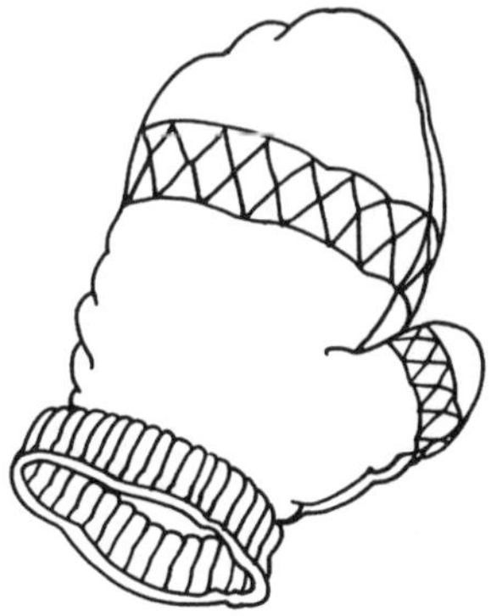

3

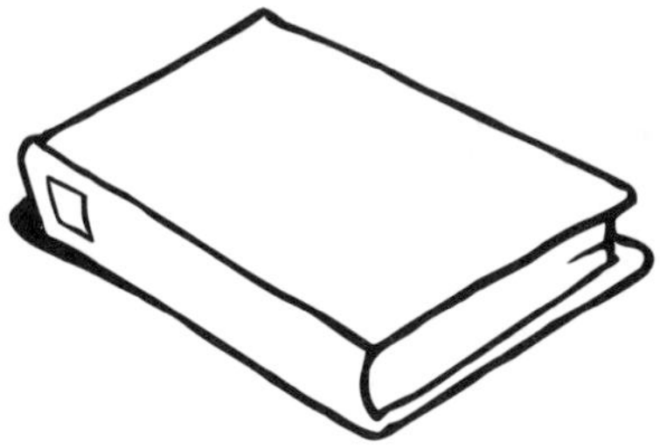

4

5

6

7

8

9

Directions: Name each picture. Have children color the pictures whose names begin with the sound for *m*.

Name ____________________

Academic Talk

Classroom Rules

5. Walk. Don't run.

6. Keep your hands to yourself.

7. Clean up.

8. ____________________

Directions: Discuss each rule with children. Have them explain why the rule is important. Discuss whether there are any missing rules. Have children choose an additional rule, draw a picture in the empty box, and dictate or write the final rule.

Name ______________________________

Academic Talk

Classroom Rules

1. Raise your hand to talk.

2. Listen carefully to others.

3. Take turns.

4. Share.

Directions: Discuss each rule with children. Have them explain why the rule is important.